Prehistoric Animals and Plants

Prehistoric Animals and Plants

by Josef Beneš
illustrated by Zdeněk Burian

HAMLYN
London · New York · Sydney · Toronto

Translated by Margot Schierlová

Line drawings by Anna Benešová
Graphic design by Stanislav Seifert

Designed and produced by Artia for
THE HAMLYN PUBLISHING GROUP LIMITED
London • New York • Sydney • Toronto
Astronaut House, Feltham, Middlesex, England

ISBN 0 600 30341 1

Printed in Czechoslovakia
3/12/01/51-01

CONTENTS

The first living organisms 6
In Palaeozoic seas 7
Vertebrates appear on the scene 11
Life migrates to the dry land 15
From fishes to amphibians 16
Permian reptiles 19
The world in the Triassic period 20
Testudinates and their history 22
Amphibians of the Triassic swamps 23
Mesozoic giants 23
Reptiles of the Mesozoic seas 25
Reptiles conquer the air 26
The first birds 26
The first mammals 28
The Earth's recent history 29
Tertiary amphibians and reptiles 31
The avian world 32
The first successful mammals 32
Mammals acquire their present form 40
The age of mammoths 43
Plates 48
Table of geological eras and periods 305
Bibliography 306
Index 308

The first living organisms

It is believed that life first began to stir on the Earth as long as three and a half to four milliard years ago. Our knowledge of this earliest period in the Earth's history, the Precambrian era, is very meagre for the amount of direct evidence, obtainable from the study of rocks of organic origin and the study of very primitive recent organisms, is limited.

Primitive organisms (Procaryota), whose bodies were composed of one or more protein molecules, originated about 2,300 million years ago. They did not possess a nucleus that was clearly divided off from the rest of the cell matter, and they did not have any other intracellular differentiation, nor did they have their protoplasm separated from the environment by a cell membrane. We know very little about the mode of life of Archaeozoic Procaryota. One thing that we do know is that the atmosphere in those days was devoid of oxygen, so that aerobic respiration was impossible, and primitive organisms acquired vitally necessary energy by fermentation processes. About two milliard years ago, bacteria-like unicellular organisms capable of assimilation (synthesis of organic substances from carbon dioxide and water with the aid of solar radiation) and blue-green, or other primitive algae, evolved. The assimilatory activity of these 'pre-plants' caused oxygen to be released into the atmosphere. We surmise that, about 1,800 million years ago, the amount of oxygen in the atmosphere rose to such an extent that it allowed a change from fermentative metabolism to aerobic respiration—a qualitatively and quantitatively higher source of energy than fermentation. With a more efficient source of energy, multicellular organisms were then able to evolve. Unicellular organisms slowly evolved into multicellular ones along many parallel, but independent, lines. An example of one of these separate groups is that comprising the sponges, which have stayed permanently at a very low phylogenetic level.

At the transition from the Precambrian era to the Cambrian period, about 600 million years ago, a further increase in the atmospheric oxygen level facilitated the synthesis of collagen, the organic basis for the formation of a skeleton. At the outset of the Cambrian period, some animals also developed the ability to reinforce their outer or inner skeleton with mineral substances, such as silica, calcium carbonate or calcium phosphate. The mineralized skeleton was capable of fossilization. The result was a 'fossil records explosion', since many different groups of organisms in existence at that time, independently of each other, acquired the ability to form a mineralized skeleton.

The number of Precambrian fossil finds is small compared with that of the Phanerozoic. The vast majority are single finds, isolated both in time and locality: finds of large complexes (associations) of fossil organisms are very rare indeed. The best preserved—and probably the most recently discovered—Precambrian complex is the one from the Ediacara Hills in Australia (Plate 1, p. 49). Although the Ediacara complex probably represents only the last phase of life prior to the Cambrian, it gives us a glimpse of the little known world of organisms living before the 'fossil records explosion'.

In Palaeozoic seas

The basic trends of the evolution of organisms were already established in the Proterozoic (Precambrian) era. They included the change from unicellular to multicellular organisms and the development, in multicellular organisms, of a spatially organized body. Spatial organization was accompanied by the specialization of nutrition to autotrophic (assimilatory) or heterotrophic (the acquisition of organic substances from other organisms). In this way the organic world split up into two types of organisms—plants and animals. At first the two types differed very little from each other, but they evolved along such dissimilar lines that plants and animals today represent two distinctly different forms of living matter. In plants, evolution led to the formation of root and leaf organs, while in animals it led to the formation of locomotor and sensory organs and organs for the mechanical and chemical processing of food.

Animals began to evolve during the Proterozoic, so that in Palaeozoic seas we already encounter a number of independent phyla at different stages of evolution.

Sponges (Plate 2, p. 51) have a hollow body with two layers of relatively independent cells not yet united as true tissue. They evolved some time during the Proterozoic and have persisted in virtually the same form ever since. As far as we know, they did not give rise to any other group of animals; they represent an isolated branch of the phylogenetic tree. However, they do provide us with an example of the level of animal life attained in the Precambrian.

Coelenterates (the word means 'hollow body' or 'hollow intestine') are a group of animals with a wealth of form. They evidently originated in late Precambrian seas (Plate 1, p. 49). Their pitcher-like body, the coelenteron, is composed of two layers of cells. The outer layer, the ectoderm, protects the animal, while the inner layer, the endoderm, has alimentary and reproductive function. The body cavity opens on to the surface by means of a mouth which takes in food and ejects waste matter and is surrounded by a wreath of tentacles. As distinct from sponges, coelenterates have muscle and nerve cells and their ectoderm can secrete a horny or chalky case capable of fossilization. Three main trends can be followed in the evolution of coelenterates. Polyps have retained the original shape of the phylum and are usually quite small. Medusae, or jellyfish, (Plate 3, p. 53) have specialized in a planktonic (drifting) mode of life, while corals and sea-anemones (Plate 7, p. 61) are the most highly specialized form of coelenterate.

The simple organization of the coelenteron prevented the animal from developing a large body. The single opening for the intake of food and ejection of the indigestible

8

remains does not allow either the ingestion of a large amount of food or continuous digestion. Furthermore, food is taken up by the individual cells straight from the gut cavity and there is no system of nutrient transport. The development of a worm-like body in the form of a tube with an opening at either end, with the possibility of continuous digestion of food, was thus a great advance in animal evolution. This type of body proved to be so successful and plastic that it was subsequently modified rather than undergoing any fundamental changes. Worm-like animals underwent an explosive evolution during the Proterozoic era and by the beginning of the Palaeozoic the first stages in the evolution of invertebrates were well over and the Palaeozoic seas were already inhabited by their highly specialized descendants, the most important of which are given below.

Brachiopods (Plate 6, p. 59) have fringed, arm-like appendages with which they stir up the water and drive food towards their mouth. They evolved some time during the Proterozoic, developed rapidly during the Cambrian and were abundant throughout the whole of the Palaeozoic. They began to decline at the end of the Palaeozoic and have done so ever since. They have a chalky or horny shell similar to that of bivalves, but evolutionally they are a separate and isolated group.

Molluscs, which are now thought to have evolved from a flatworm-like ancestor before the Cambrian, are a very interesting group. They are thought to have separated from these worm-like ancestors early in the evolution of a segmented body. Some primitive forms have certain characters of metamery but none are known to be fully segmented. Their main characters are their mantle cavity and shell. Many forms have a head with sensory organs (eyes, feelers) and their body is protected by a hard calcareous shell of very variable shape, which in some forms has been secondarily lost. Molluscs are divided into several systematic groups representing the main evolutionary trends. Bivalves (Bivalvia) and Snails (Gastropoda) be-

9

came widespread early in the Palaeozoic and have been the most common marine invertebrates since the Mesozoic; snails actually invaded terrestrial habitats. The third major molluscan group, the Cephalopoda, have highly developed sensory organs (they have the same type of eyes as vertebrates) and in the Palaeozoic areas their characteristic representatives were the orthoceratids (Plate 8, p. 63).

In morphological and evolutionary terms the most varied group of invertebrates are the arthropods. They evolved from aquatic annelid worms some time before the Cambrian period, and during their subsequent evolution their nervous system retained the same structure as that of worms and their body remained distinctly segmented. Unlike worms, however, they acquired the ability to reinforce their body surface with a calcium carbonate or a chitin case. The case forms an outer skeleton (exoskeleton) to which muscles forming a characteristic locomotor system are attached. The earliest arthropods were probably not very different from worms and had one pair of limbs on each segment (as is still the case in centipedes, for example). Arthropods are exceptionally adaptable and have therefore penetrated into every type of environment. Apart from vertebrates, they are the only group which colonized the dry land on a large scale and it was only their small size (determined by their exoskeleton and their tracheal respiratory system) which prevented them from becoming the dominant type of terrestrial animal.

Trilobites are important and characteristic arthropods which occurred in Palaeozoic seas (Plates 4—6, pp. 55—59). Their early evolution is obscure and probably extends far back into the Precambrian era, since by the beginning of the Cambrian period the trilobites were a fully evolved and highly specialized group. Although some research workers regard them as the ancestors of various groups of Recent arthropods, insects for example, it is becoming increasingly clear that the trilobites form an independent group whose evolution ended during the Palaeozoic and which played no part in the evolution of any other group.

Echinoderms (Plates 6 and 9, pp. 59, 64—65) are an isolated and very characteristic group. The development and structure of their embryos resemble those of the more highly organized animals such as the Chordata, and are evidence of a relatively high grade of phylogenesis in this group. Later, however, mainly as a result of a sessile mode of life, secondarily primitive, that is degenerate, characters, such as radial symmetry and the loss of sensory organs, began to prevail among echinoderms. Sessile forms such as sea-lilies reached the peak of their evolution in the Palaeozoic era and some groups did not survive it. Mobile forms such as sea-urchins, sea-stars and holothurians, which constitute the majority of living echinoderms, began to flourish at the beginning of the Mesozoic era.

Vertebrates appear on the scene

The morphological evolution of invertebrates was determined by the development of an exoskeleton (test, shell, etc.), whereas vertebrates are characterized by the development of an internal skeleton (endoskeleton). Compared with molluscs' shells, the endoskeleton is relatively light. Its parts are joined together by articulations (joints), which do not restrict the animal's movements and allow continuous postnatal development and growth without the need of larval stages and metamorphoses. This was a great advance in evolution, allowing vertebrates to attain the highest degree of physical, physiological and mental perfection.

The theory that vertebrates are phylogenetically descended from marine annelid worms took root in the last decades of the nineteenth century. It is based on certain morphological similarities between annelids and vertebrates. Annelids have a bilaterally symmetrical body and, unlike the sessile forms of other invertebrates, are capable of free movement. Their body is segmented (the verte-

11

brate backbone has been interpreted as the last vestige of this segmentation) and they have a central nervous system analogous to the spinal cord, with a cerebral ganglion. In other respects they are dissimilar, however. In annelids, the whole of the body is segmented, from the epidermis to the alimentary tube, the excretory organs and the sex glands (gonads). The nervous system lies ventrally to the alimentary tube, i.e. on the under side of the body, while in vertebrates it lies dorsally, i.e. along the back. One might say that a vertebrate is an annelid turned over on to its back, but there is no phylogenetic evidence of any such reversal. Moreover, annelids display no signs of incipient formation of an internal skeleton.

A new theory of the common origin of chordates and echinoderms has lately started to acquire popularity. The apparently paradoxical relationship between vertebrates and echinoderms implicit in this theory is nevertheless supported by abundant palaeontological and zoological evidence, such as the embryonic development of these groups. These groups presumably all originated in the Precambrian from a primitively organized animal resembling a coelenterate. Round its mouth this sessile animal had a tentacled ridge known as a lophophore, which drove oxygenated water (needed for respiration) and food towards the mouth. Two phylogenetic lines lead from this animal — one to echinoderms, whose evolution took a completely different turn, and the other to *Rhabdopleura*, a hemichordate. The first step towards the evolution of chordates occurred when the lophophore was replaced by a gill-filter, formed by perforation of the gullet by gill-slits. Perfection of the gill-filter made the lophophore superfluous and it disappeared. It was precisely this reduction of

Fig. 1. Origination of vertebrates
A. Primitive sessile animal with whirling ciliary apparatus ('wheel animal') B. *Rhabdopleura* C. *Pterobranchia* D. Primitive echinoderm E. Initial form after loss of antennae F. *Balanoglossus* G. Primitive tunicate H. Recent ascidian K. Recent salpa M. Free-swimming ascidian larva N. Primitive fish-like vertebrate with gill-openings O. Lancelet P. Primitive fish

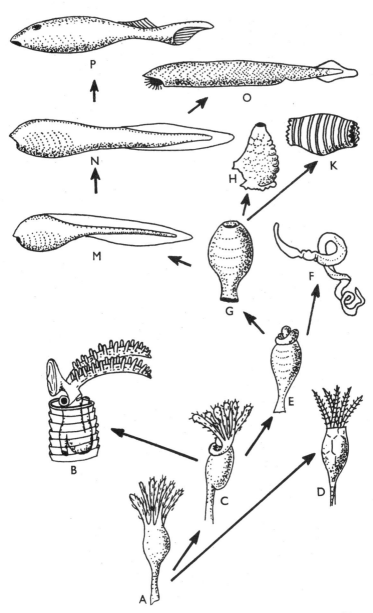

the lophophore that made motion possible, since the arms of the lophophore were very vulnerable to damage. The genus *Balanoglossus,* whose members have a worm-like body and a 'collar' reinforced with a cartilaginous disc (hemichord), has remained at this stage of evolution, without a lophophore, down to the present day. In ascidians (tunicates or urochordates), the gill apparatus was improved still further. The adult animal is sessile, but the larva can move about freely and resembles a tadpole. Animals at the next stage of evolution retain their locomotor apparatus, including a dorsal notochord, into adulthood. This is actually neoteny, the preservation of juvenile characters as evolutionally progressive characters, a fairly common phenomenon in phylogenesis. They also continue to breathe through a gill-filter. This stage of evolution is represented by the lancelet (a cephalochordate), even though it has deviated somewhat from the main evolutionary trend, since the adult animal lives buried in the sand.

The development of a locomotor apparatus was the basis on which fishes evolved. An axial skeleton or backbone developed around the notochord and a cranial skeleton around the brain centre, while the locomotor organs were reinforced by a limb skeleton, which was at first unconnected with the axial skeleton. The basic vertebrate skeleton is found in fishes. In higher vertebrates (amphibians, reptiles, birds and mammals), inherited structural elements are only partially modified (this does not apply to the other parts of the body and to embryogenesis, of course). The 'fishes' comprise a large and heterogeneous group of animals at different stages of phylogenetic development, from primitive chordates to true vertebrates with a bony skeleton. Modern systematics divide fishes into five groups—jawless fishes, Agnatha (Plate 10, p. 67); armoured fishes, Placodermi (Plate 11, p. 69); fishes with a cartilaginous skeleton, Chondrichthyes or Elasmobranchii (Plates 12 and 13, pp. 71, 72—73); bony fishes, Osteichthyes or Actinopterygii; and the lung-fishes, Crossopterygii. The first traces of the existence of piscine vertebrates

14

date back to the Ordovician period. Jawless fishes are known from the Silurian period and ossification of the skeleton took place, to unequal degrees in different taxonomic groups, during the Devonian period. The phylogenetically most important group of fishes are the crossopterygians, about which we shall have more to say later on.

Life migrates to the dry land

At the end of the early Palaeozoic, that is, at the end of the Silurian and the beginning of the Devonian period, mountain-building movements altered the configuration of the continents and seas, especially the shallow littoral parts, and were instrumental in moving life from the water to the dry land. Plants preceded animals in this migration; recently the remains of what were unquestionably terrestrial plants were found in rocks of Silurian age. Initially plants colonized the marshy ground beside the water and only then moved further away from it. This whole process of colonization of the dry land was not a steady, continuous one, but took place independently among the different plant groups at a number of periods of geological time, when here and there certain forms succeeded in taking hold. Extensive areas of vegetation which can loosely be described as 'forests' are known to have existed from the Devonian period. These sections of silicified plant remains from Scottish Devonian formations have been studied under the microscope. The anatomical structure thus revealed showed these plants to be primitive cryptogamous vascular ones. They were by no means large; they grew from creeping rootstocks, usually to a height of a few decimetres, but never to more than two or three metres. These primitive cryptogamous plants later gave rise to club-mosses, horsetails and ferns, which were the characteristic plants of the late Devonian and especially of the Carboniferous period.

Genuine forests are encountered from the Carboniferous period onwards. The most important types of vegetation in these formations were tree-like club-mosses and horsetails attaining a height of up to thirty metres. The most attractive and most varied constituents of Carboniferous forests were ferns, with a wealth of forms ranging from small herbaceous kinds to numerous arboreal types. For countless ages the remains of their branches, leaves and stems went on sinking into the mud of the Carboniferous swamps. It was these layers of vegetable matter which were later formed into the coal after which the Carboniferous period is named.

The growth of forests was a very important factor in the evolution of terrestrial animals, because it opened up new, uninhabited ecological niches. The first creatures to take to the dry land were gastropods and arthropods; arthropods' high adaptability enabling them to occupy in a short time all types of environment. The evolution of insects probably began in the Silurian or the Devonian period, since evidence of the existence of wingless insects has been found in Devonian strata, but at present we know nothing of the earliest stages of this evolution. The rapid evolution of the insects, which began at the end of the Carboniferous period, continued into the Permian period. Since then they have not undergone any further important evolutionary changes, but have increased enormously in numbers and distribution (Plate 14, p. 74).

From fishes to amphibians

Vertebrates are the other group which dominate the dry land. The first terrestrial vertebrates evolved during the transition from the Devonian to the Carboniferous period and the main role in the transformation of the fish to a four-legged terrestrial animal was played by the group of fishes known as crossopterygians (Plate 15, p. 77). These evolved during the Devonian period and originally lived in fresh water. In the Mesozoic they migrated to the sea, where today one genus (*Latimeria*—the coelacanth) still lives, a relic of a bygone age. The characteristic feature of crossopterygians is the peculiar structure of their broad-based paired fins, which are long and composed of webbing, reinforced with spines. The fin muscles are distributed round the spines outside the fish's trunk, like the limb muscles of quadrupeds, so that the fins have muscular shafts, as it were. In addition to gills, crossopterygians also possess primitive auxiliary lungs which can take up atmospheric oxygen. Their conical teeth are covered with enamel and resemble the teeth of amphibians in structure. Crossopterygians flourished for a short time only, but as ancestors of the amphibians they are of great phylogenetic significance.

The oldest amphibians—and hence the oldest terrestrial vertebrates—were the stegocephalians. They are thought to have evolved from crossopterygians which lived in shallow water and swamps, and were thus subjected to fluctuating water levels and even drought conditions. Their first acquaintance with the dry land would have been more or less forced on them, when they were obliged to crawl from one pool to another as each in turn dried up. Their muscular fins would have been a great help, since they could be used for locomotion on the land. In time, the length of their enforced stay on the dry land increased, and since the drying pools were full of living and dead creatures, there was a good source of easily accessible food for an animal that could tolerate the drought. It was in this way that the gradual change from an aquatic to a terrestrial way of life was effected, but the process was very slow and was also incomplete, since only the adult animal became fully adapted to the new environment, the early development of the offspring still taking place in the water.

The environmental change in the life of these creatures was accompanied by a number of changes in body structure. Fishes breathe oxygen dissolved in water. As the length of time spent on the dry land grew longer, brachial

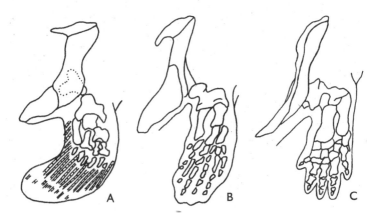

Fig. 2. The change from the water to the dry land
  A. pectoral fin of the crossopterygian fish *Eusthenopteron* (Devonian),
  B. fore limb of the stegocephalian *Eogyynus* (Carboniferous), C. fore
  limb of the stegocephalian *Eryops* (Permian)

(gill) respiration was gradually superseded by pulmonary respiration. Proper lungs developed by invagination of the gullet.

Another important change was the liberation of the head. When the now superfluous gills regressed, the opercular bones and gill arches also disappeared and their place was taken by the otic notches typical of early reptiles. Part of the spine—the neck—was left free between the skull and the fore limbs. During further evolution the cervical ribs also disappeared and the first vertebra was connected to the skull by a joint. This allowed the head movements essential for existence on the dry land.

The limbs likewise underwent pronounced changes. In water the body is buoyant and the fins only propel it, but on dry land the limbs carry the weight of the whole body. In stegocephalians, the fin bases were gradually transformed into a shoulder and a pelvic girdle. The fin rays broke up transversely into a few articulated parts and their number was reduced, usually to five. Lengthening and thickening of the proximal parts of the fore limb gave rise to the humerus, the radius and the ulna and in the hind limb to the femur, the tibia and the fibula. Body weight was diminished by reduction of the scaly armour, which in most stegocephalians persisted only on the head and abdomen. The uncovering of the epidermis in turn permitted cutaneous respiration, thereby supplementing the function of the relatively poorly developed lungs.

Stegocephalians inhabited swamps and water's edge, to which their embryonic development kept them bound. The oldest stegocephalians, whose relationship to the crossopterygians was still manifest in many respects, are known from late Devonian strata (Plate 16, p. 78). Their heyday was the Carboniferous period and from the beginning of the Permian they started to decline (Plates 17—19, pp. 81—84).

Permian reptiles

In the Carboniferous period, the vegetation spread further away from the large sheets of water and the animal population moved with it. This naturally meant that the animals had to become independent of the aquatic environment. The first group of vertebrates to succeed in this were the reptiles. They evolved from Carboniferous stegocephalians and their evolution was determined by a number of changes in their body structure and habits. The fine stegocephalian scales disappeared and their place was taken by a horny epidermis which protected the body against excessive loss of water. This virtually put an end to cutaneous respiration, but pulmonary respiration was perfected and the blood circulation improved. The limbs also underwent certain changes. The body was raised above the ground, bringing faster and more economic movement, as energy losses caused by the friction entailed in crawling disappeared. The neck also developed and grew longer and more flexible, thereby increasing the mobility of the head. The greatest changes occurred in embryonic development. Reptiles no longer laid their eggs in the water, but buried them in rotting plant debris, or in sand or soil. The embryo was wrapped in an embryonic (amniotic) membrane and the aquatic environment was replaced by the fluid in the amniotic cavity of the egg. The reptilian egg is prevented from drying up and from mechanical injury by a leathery envelope or a shell. Newly hatched reptiles are minute replicas of their parents, the larval stage having been dispensed with.

The first reptiles evolved at the end of the Carboniferous period, but did not begin to flourish until the early Permian period, when several evolutionary trends can be distinguished. The most primitive reptiles include the cotylosaurs (Plates 20 and 23, pp. 87, 92), which were mostly small, clumsy types, still closely resembling stegocephalians. The structure of the skull and vertebrae was very primitive and the humerus and femur were horizontal (the limbs could only raise the body from the ground). Cotylosaurs reached the peak of their development in the Permian period. They closely resembled pelycosaurs (Plates 21, 22, pp. 88—89, 91), known from upper Permian and Triassic strata. Very soon they broke up into several evolutionary branches, the most interesting of which, for us, is the line of the mammalian reptiles (Plate 24, p. 94). While this line pursued the development of mammalian characters, other branches became highly specialized. The mesosaurs (Plate 25, p. 97) returned to their ancestral habitat, the water.

The world in the Triassic period

The Mesozoic is an interesting era in the Earth's history. From the phylogenetic aspect it is a truly 'mediaeval' era—an era which paved the way for great changes. It marks the peak of evolutionary trends embarked on in the Palaeozoic and its chief feature was the evolution of a tremendous number of groups of reptiles, which colonized every available corner of the dry land as well as the air and water.

The Triassic period—the earliest division of the Meso-zoic—was formerly neglected by the scientists. It is true that it cannot boast huge dinosaurs and other striking groups of animals, as the Jurassic and the Cretaceous peri-ods can, but it was during the Triassic that these groups started to evolve. The Permian mesosaurs' example of a return to an aquatic environment was followed during the Triassic by other branches of the reptile group. The most interesting and most highly specialized were the ich-thyosaurs, the 'fish lizards' (Plate 28, p. 102). They looked like dolphins, but the two are not in any way related. The skull and vertebrae of ichthyosaurs resembled those of the primitive stegocephalians from which the ichthyosaurs had evolved. They had no neck and had reduced hind limbs, but their fin-like fore limbs were very powerful, and their embryonic development took place inside ,the mother's body. It is not clear exactly when the evolution of the ichthyosaurs began; they appeared in the middle of the Triassic period as a fully evolved group and survived, practically unchanged, up to the late Cretaceous, when they died out without leaving any descendants. Plesiosaurs (Plate 29, p. 104), on the other hand, had a long serpentine neck and their limbs were converted to paddles. They are related to the placodonts (Plates 26 and 27, pp. 99, 100), testudinate-like reptiles that lived mainly on molluscs (see below).

The theriodonts, mammal-like reptiles, are an evolution-ally very important group. Independently of each other, the various lines all more or less closely resembled the first mammals: to differing extents the brain, teeth, jaws and other parts of the skeleton of these reptiles underwent 'mammalization'. The herbivorous dicynodonts (Plate 30, p. 107) also showed some mammalian characters, but did not resemble mammals as closely as did the carnivorous theriodonts. The late Triassic ictidosaurians showed an almost completely mammal-like structure and are often indeed classified as true mammals. The similarities be-tween different groups of mammal-like reptiles raise the obvious question of whether mammals evolved as a single phylogenetic line from one ancestor, or as a polyphyletic group from several ancestral lines. Unfortunately, we know nothing about the embryonic development of theriodonts, and therefore are unable to answer these vital questions.

The thecodonts (Plate 31, p. 108) are another evolutionally very important group. They were small, lizard-like Triassic reptiles which gave rise to a number of important reptile groups, such as dinosaurs, plesiosaurs and crocodiles, and possibly to birds as well.

Testudinates and their history

Testudinates are a sharply defined group of rather primitive, but highly specialized reptiles. They probably originated in the Permian period from small cotylosaurs. Their direct ancestors—belonging to the hypothetical group Protestudinata—were small reptiles with a lizard-like and relatively heavily built body like the majority of cotylosaurs. Their body was covered with dermal plates (as in crocodiles) and with rows of scales. Protestudinates, like all primitive reptiles, probably originally lived in swamps, but as their evolution progressed they migrated to the dry land. The environmental change was associated with the acquisition of dermal armour produced by widening and union of the originally unconnected rows of dermal plates. This armour was evidently formed for the purpose of protecting these slowly-moving animals; it was also developed in other groups of reptiles (Plate 27, p. 100). At subsequent stages of evolution the number of dermal plates diminished and the internal skeleton was gradually connected to the armour. Evidently at the same time, testudinates also developed the ability to withdraw their head and limbs into the shell. The evolutionary process was a long one, as seen from *Triassochelys* (Plate 32, p. 111). A creature which was still unable to withdraw its head into its shell, it is regarded as the last stage in the evolution of protestudinates. Some lines of testudinates, at a relatively early stage of evolution, returned to the sea (Plate 33, p. 113).

Amphibians of the Triassic swamps

Amphibians were the dominant vertebrates in the Carboniferous, but gradually, during the Permian, they declined in numbers and importance, while the reptiles grew in numbers and became increasingly diversified until they in turn dominated the landscape in the Triassic period. The amphibians' most conservative branch, the stereospondylous stegocephalians (Plate 35, pp. 116—117), still survived, however, and during the Triassic period produced forms the size of a crocodile, but even these died out at the end of the Triassic, without leaving any descendants. The only branch of amphibians to keep a place of any importance among the animal associations of more recent geological periods were frogs (Plate 34, p. 115), which probably evolved, during the Carboniferous period, from stegocephalians. During their evolution, their tail gradually regressed and their limbs (especially the hind ones) lengthened, as an adaptation for leaping. Their skeleton became lighter, with their ribs getting shorter and some of their skull bones being replaced by cartilage or simply by a strong membrane. We know very little about the evolution of frogs in the Mesozoic era, but Tertiary finds are more common.

Mesozoic giants

Dinosaurs (Plates 36—45, pp. 118—137), the descendants of small Triassic thecodonts, are probably the best known and to many people the most exciting group of reptiles. They make up the largest and most diverse group and comprise animals of the greatest size ever attained by reptiles and are often of a bizarre nature with bodies covered by horny outgrowths or armour. Carnivorous types had extremely well developed dentition. Alongside these huge forms there were also small terrestrial and arboreal forms of dinosaur (Plate 46, p. 138). Dinosaurs evolved during the Triassic period, but reached the peak of their development in the Jurassic and Cretaceous periods. Their extinction at the end of the Cretaceous has been a subject of numerous conjectures based on more or less sound scientific foundations. There is actually nothing at all catastrophic about the extinction of the dinosaurs, which persisted for several million years. Although no-one knows for certain, their extinction may have been largely due to climatic changes and reorganization of the continents at the end of the Cretaceous period, these climatic changes being accompanied by changes in the vegetation. The era of recent plants, the Cainophytic era, can be said to have begun during the late Cretaceous period, unlike the era of recent animal life, the Cainozoic era, which began with the onset of the Tertiary era. Gymnosperm plants declined and angiosperms started to flourish, so that dinosaurs which lived on a specialized gymnosperm diet found less and less to eat. The climatic changes themselves likewise had an adverse effect on the dinosaurs. As poikilothermic animals (animals with a variable body temperature), they were unable to cope with seasonal changes in temperature. Their specialization and consequent lack of adaptability prevented them from acquiring the ability to physiologically regulate their body temperature, an ability possessed by homoiothermic birds and mammals. The young animals were affected most by the differences between summer and winter. In addition, with the increasingly cold winters, the plants lost their leaves in the autumn and the huge dinosaurs, unable to hibernate, were doomed to starvation. The decrease in the herbivorous dinosaur population led directly to extinction of the carnivorous dinosaurs and to the collapse of the whole animal association. It is true that

24

the negative changes which caused the terrestrial dinosaurs to die out could not have caused extinction of the marine plesiosaurs, ichthyosaurs and mosasaurs, etc., which died out at the same time. Therefore, there may be many factors concerning the extinction of the dinosaurs in general which we still do not know about.

Reptiles of the Mesozoic seas

Several lines of reptiles returned to an aquatic habitat in the Mesozoic seas. The changes took place at different times and the animals, independently of each other, attained different degrees of adaptation. Crocodiles (Plates 47 and 48, pp. 141, 142) evolved from thecodonts during the late Triassic period and altered very little in subsequent geological periods.

Mosasaurs (Plates 49 and 50, pp. 145—147) appeared during the early Cretaceous period and invaded the seas. They evolved from a group of reptiles which is represented today by the monitor lizards and they attained the peak of their development in the late Cretaceous. It is interesting to note that, as well as traces of various injuries, the fossil bones of mosasaurs also show signs of mild and severe diseases, especially when they were at their acme. According to some scientists, it was precisely this period, when they lived under ideal conditions, without natural predators, that was crucial to their final demise. Weak and defective individuals gave rise to new generations whose physical resistance was likewise mostly very poor. All that was then needed were slight modifications of their biotope, such as climatic and geographical changes, to cause the mosasaurs to die out in a relatively short time, despite the fact that these changes would have affected the sea less than the land.

We have already mentioned the plesiosaurs (Plates 51—53, pp. 148—152) in the chapter on Triassic reptiles. Their evolution reached its culmination in the Jurassic and

Cretaceous periods, but in the early Tertiary seas there was no longer any sign of them. The ichthyosaurs (Plates 54 and 55, pp. 155, 157), which flourished before and during the Triassic period, were beautifully adapted to an aquatic environment. The Jurassic was their peak period and they disappeared in the late Cretaceous.

Reptiles conquer the air

In the Mesozoic era, reptiles conquered the air, as well as the land and the water. These reptiles formed a specialized group and are known as pterosaurs (Plates 56—59, pp. 159—165). They were able to fly like bats by means of membranous webbing, and they also had many features in common with birds, but they are a separate evolutionary branch altogether and are not connected with birds in any way. They lived only during the Jurassic and Cretaceous periods and at the end of the latter they died out without leaving any descendants. When the first birds appeared, in the Jurassic period, the pterosaurs were at the peak of their development and birds did not represent a danger to them. In the Cretaceous period, however, birds were already expert fliers and it is possible that in competition with them the pterosaurs were the losers. The many climatic and geographical changes which took place at the end of the Cretaceous period were again probably some of the reasons why this distinctive group of reptiles died out.

The first birds

At present we know very little about fossil birds. That is not because they did not exist, but because the probability of tiny, hollow avian bones becoming fossilized is very small. Such bones as have been preserved have either been found isolated, or clumped together in debris, from which it is hard to extract them whole and piece them together. Finds of complete skeletons are few and far between. These isolated finds must be re-assembled, therefore, using various theories with the inevitable hypothetical links. The beginning of the evolution of birds must, it is now thought, be sought among Triassic thecodonts of the order Pseudosuchia, for the pseudosuchian skeleton bears a whole series of avian characters. The crucial point in the transformation of the reptile to the bird was the formation of feathers from reptilian scales. The transformation probably did not take place all at once, over the whole of the body. Even Recent birds still have scales on their tarsi and in the extinct *Archaeopteryx* they also covered the head. The origination of feathers was evidently associated with an increase in the blood circulation and with stabilization of the body temperature. We presume that pseudosuchians gave rise to the hypothetical *'Proavis'* (Plate 60, p. 167) which possessed a parachute apparatus formed by widening and lengthening of the scales on the sides of the body and limbs. *'Proavis'* was still a flightless reptile, which could only climb trees and glide from branch to branch. The next stage was the hypothetical *'Eoavis',* which was capable of awkward, fluttering flight. The third—and palaeontologically verified—stage was *Archaeopteryx* (Plate 61, p. 169), at present known only from four finds near Solnhofen in Bavaria (Germany). The evolution of *'Proavis'* to *Archaeopteryx* took place during the late Triassic on early Jurassic period.

In the Cretaceous period, birds underwent some 'modernization'. A large ridge, typical of birds, developed on their breastbone for insertion of the flight muscles. Their caudal vertebrae fused to form the pygostyle, around which the tail feathers were arranged. Their skull bones also united and their jaws were transformed to a beak. Finds of birds in Cretaceous strata are more numerous and more diverse than in Jurassic strata, but they again mostly consist of single bones, which are hard to classify. The majority come from aquatic birds and the number of bones belonging to terrestrial species is very small.

The next great step in the evolution of birds took place at the end of the Cretaceous period and at the beginning of the Tertiary (Cainozoic) era, when a number of groups still living today evolved. Grebes and pelicans are known from the late Cretaceous period and birds of prey from the Palaeocene. The other modern groups are known from Eocene, or at the latest from Oligocene, strata.

The first mammals

Mammals are a line of vertebrates which have achieved the highest grade of evolution to date. Our information on the initial evolution of this group is at present very meagre, because the small size of the first mammals did not provide sufficient material for fossilization. From the incomplete skeletal remains which have been found, it is sometimes hard to tell whether the creature was an advanced reptile or a primitive mammal, since the bones do not show whether it was viviparous or not.

Mammals originated from Triassic theriodonts, mammal-like reptiles descended from Permian pelycosaurs. The reason for the transformation of reptiles to mammals is not clear. It was not the outcome of adaptation to an environmental change, since mammals evolved at the same time as the more modern types of Mesozoic reptiles. While reptiles flourished during the Mesozoic era, mammals formed only an insignificant part of its fauna, with few species and individuals. It was not until the end of the Cretaceous period, when many reptiles had died out, that mammals began to fill the ecological niches thus left vacant and passed through a number of rapid evolutionary changes.

This phase of mammalian evolution culminated in formation of the pre-insectivore group, from which a direct line leads to the insectivores and on to the primates.

The Earth's recent history

The Tertiary (Cainozoic) era was truly a modern age in the Earth's history, especially as regards plants and animals. Great palaeogeographic changes were the forces which led to the 'modernization' of the organic world.

The background against which life evolved was the Earth's crust, together with the atmosphere (the Earth's gaseous envelope) and the hydrosphere (the Earth's watery envelope). The actual crust is split up into individual blocks (platforms), forming continents. The spaces between them are filled with water (the oceans).

Our conception of the configuration of the continents and seas in early geological eras is at present only vague. It can be claimed with some degree of probability that 200 million years and more ago the continental blocks all formed a single whole or a 'supercontinent', which geologists term Pangea, surrounded by a single ocean, Panthalassa. About 200 million years ago this supercontinent began to crack and break up into individual blocks, resembling in shape and size the present continents.

The geographical position of these blocks in relation to the poles and equator differed considerably from the present situation. The various blocks began to move at different rates and in different directions. At the end of the Triassic period (about 195 million years ago), Pangea divided into a northern part known as Laurasia (present North America, Europe and Asia) and a southern part known as Gondwanaland (the continents of the southern hemisphere). The Indian shield broke away from Gondwanaland and started to shift northwards, while in the Cretaceous period South America and Africa parted company, South America moving west and Africa north. At the beginning of the Tertiary era, about sixty-five million years ago, the Indian shield was united with Asia, and Africa moved up close to Europe. This was naturally manifested in intense mountain-forming activity on the various continents.

In the Mesozoic era, the plant world was characterized by the disappearance or numerical reduction of cryptogamous plants, which had been predominant in the preceding Palaeozoic era. Their place was taken in the Mesozoic by phanerogamous plants. Palaeogeographic and climatic changes played some role in this process, but most important was the fact that phanerogams had a number of advantages over cryptogams. The formation, on the maternal plant, of a seed with a supply of nutrients for the embryo of the new plant, stronger wood and a better root and transport system helped to make phanerogams independent of an aquatic environment and able to spread further on to the dry land. At the beginning of the Mesozoic era, the main phanerogamous plants were gymnosperms, i.e. conifers and cycads, which were joined in the Jurassic period by bennettites (Bennettitaceae), herbs or stumpy trees with bulging or cylindrical stems and cycad-like leaves. An unusual feature of bennettites was their reproductive organs, which resembled the flowers of angiospermous plants.

A radical change occurred in the plant world in the late Cretaceous period, with the spread of angiospermous (flowering) plants, which today form the majority of all plants. The ovules are enclosed in the ovaries (seed-cases) and the male cells (pollen grains) are formed in the anthers. The reproductive organs are surrounded and concealed by petals and sometimes also by sepals. The question of the origin and formation of the most primitive flowering plants is a very hard one to answer. They appeared quite suddenly, in large quantities, in the late Cretaceous period. This shows that they must have had a long evolutionary history behind them, but we know next to nothing about it. The oldest angiosperms probably existed in the early Triassic period and they must have originated and developed as a result of adaptation to a dry highland or steppe climate. This explains their rare occurrence in the pre-Cretaceous period. In the Jurassic period they infiltrated low-lying and damp regions and in the late Cretaceous they appeared everywhere. Their qualitative (phylogenetic) development evidently took place much sooner. Certain Recent genera, such as plane-trees, magnolias, fig-trees, and tulip-trees, already existed in the late Cretaceous period, while in the Tertiary era they began to flourish and to compete successfully with gymnosperms. Angiosperms were soon able to cope with altered geographical conditions and, more important, with new climatic conditions. The number of Recent genera and species already present in the early Tertiary increased to include for example the briar rose, cinnamon-tree, bay-tree, walnut-tree, beech, maple, hazel and alder. Vegetation of a present-day type developed and the climatic conditions led to large plant communities being broken up into smaller associations influenced by the local situation.

Tertiary amphibians and reptiles

All palaeogeographic, climatic and vegetation changes produced important changes among animals. Less specialized forms mostly survived and in some cases, where further ecological niches became available, they produced many new races (mainly birds and mammals). Highly specialized forms did not generally survive the collapse of Mesozoic ecosystems. The effect on reptiles, which up to then had been supreme among the vertebrates, was disastrous. All that was left of the great twenty or so groups of Mesozoic reptiles were testudinates, crocodiles, lizards (including monitors) and snakes. Amphibians, which had already formed only a small portion of the early Mesozoic fauna, suffered the same fate. From the Tertiary era onwards we find only salamanders, newts and frogs, the last of which became the largest amphibian group. Some of them were the direct ancestors of today's frogs (Plate 66, p. 179), while among the salamanders, the Tertiary *Andrias scheuchzeri* (Plate 65, p. 177) became well known.

The avian world

The avian world of the Tertiary and early Quaternary era comprised all the families and genera living today, together with a number of other groups which are now extinct. Among the large avian forms, the one in which the general public is the most interested is that represented by flightless cursorial birds. These are interesting because, although they had a toothless beak, their pectoral bone was flat and not carinate. Their wings were puny or stunted. Their caudal vertebrae were not fused in a pygostyle, while their hind limbs were adapted for running (the number of toes was reduced to two) and their feathers, as distinct from those of flying birds, had a pseudo-quill as well as a quill. These features all indicate that the evolution of cursorial birds had followed an independent course for a long time. Some scientists claim that they are a completely separate phylogenetic branch and have nothing in common with other birds. We must look for their origin among the small Mesozoic dinosaurs. The moa from Madagascar and New Zealand (Plates 71—74, pp. 189—195) also belongs to the fossil cursorial birds, but the ostrich-like moas were not the only huge birds. Giant cranes also existed (Plates 68 and 69, pp. 183, 184) and their representatives were dreaded predators, while the moa was a vegetarian. The only real information we possess on smaller birds concerns aquatic birds (Plate 70, p. 187); we know very little about those which lived on dry land.

The first successful mammals

Tertiary changes brought a new group of animals—mammals—to the fore. We know that mammals evolved from rather small and very agile reptiles of the extinct suborder Theriodonta (descendants of Permian pelycosaurs). The transformation of a reptile to a mammal brought a number of changes in the organization of the body and also in various physiological functions and habits.

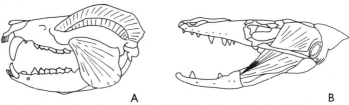

Fig. 3 Comparison of mammal's skull (A) with reptile's skull (B). Note the marked differences in the structure of the jaws and the muscles of mastication.

The most significant changes for palaeontology are naturally those which affected the parts of the body capable of fossilization, i.e. mainly the bones and the teeth. The progressive restructuring of the skull is particularly noticeable. Intensification of the function of the brain as the controlling organ was accompanied by enlargement of the brain-pan, which in evolutionally advanced forms accounted for half, or more than half, the size of the skull. The jaws and teeth also underwent considerable transformation. The function of reptilian teeth was to grip prey, whereas the function of mammals' teeth was the mechanical processing of food. This strongly influenced the rate of digestion (reptiles swallow their food whole, so that it takes a long time to digest and while this is going on the animal is usually sluggish). The altered function of the teeth was also associated with modification of the jaws and of the teeth themselves. In biting, i.e. crushing food, the jaws must exert much greater pressure than when merely seizing prey. The separate bones of the reptile's jaw fused to form the compact jaw of the mammal. The articulation of the lower jaw altered and a wide angle was formed. The muscles controlling the movements of the jaw underwent marked development (Fig. 3). The reconstruction of the teeth is interesting. From simple peg-like structures they were successively transformed to teeth with three or four cusps. Reconstruction of the teeth took place in several evolutionary lines at the same time and the range of the changes was so wide that the structure of the

33

teeth varied with the species. Mammals' teeth are thus a good criterion for systematic classification and for placing animals in natural phylogenetic orders. In the case of an unknown fossil species, they also provide a good basis for reconstruction of the animal.

Stabilization of the body temperature was a very important physiological change. It prevented the body from over-heating at high temperatures and prevented hypothermia and sluggishness when the temperature fell. Reptiles never acquired the ability to physiologically regulate their body temperature and this was evidently a weak point in competition with mammals. Stabilization of the body temperature was accompanied by a change in the body teguments. Scaly armour, which gave good protection against injury, but poor insulation against cold, was replaced by fur. It is not altogether clear how fur evolved, but it is certain that it did not, as distinct from plumage, originate as a result of transformation of reptilian scales.

Viviparity is another specific property of mammals. It avoids the vulnerable egg stage, when the embryo is defenceless. The embryo is much better protected if it develops in the mother's body, and suckling, another feature peculiar to mammals, ensures that the young are kept supplied with food until able to fend for themselves.

Four great periods of evolutionary expansion can be observed in the history of mammals—the early Mesozoic (Jurassic), late Mesozoic (Cretaceous), early Tertiary (Palaeocene to Eocene) and late Tertiary (Miocene). The forces behind this expansion were great palaeogeographic changes.

The mammals which evolved during the Jurassic period were very small. Unfortunately, we know most of them only from finds of teeth or jaws. Only a few skulls have been preserved and nothing at all is known of the rest of their skeleton. From what remains there are, we can conclude that they looked rather like shrews and they can be classified in several phylogenetic and systematic groups according to their teeth (Fig. 4).

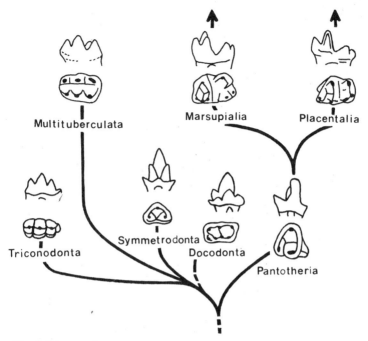

Fig. 4 Scheme of evolution of mammals' teeth (and also of Mesozoic mammals)

Primitive Jurassic triconodonts (Plate 64, p. 175) were formerly regarded as the basic type of mammal. Triconodont molars had three cusps, all in a row, and could cut food. Triconodonts may thus have been the first flesh-eating mammals. They occurred only during the Jurassic and early Cretaceous periods and today they are considered to be a blind side alley in the evolution of mammals, having no connections with the present-day fauna.

Multituberculates were specialized Jurassic mammals with differentiated (heterodontous) dentition. Their molars had a large number of cusps arranged in rows and their lower jaw was constructed like a rodent's. They seem to have been vegetarians and to have lived mainly on berries, etc. but they may also have eaten worms, snails and the like. They probably lived similarly to present-day rodents and they are the only group of the Jurassic expansion period to have survived into the early Tertiary (the Eocene). They are sometimes thought to be the ancestors of the monotremes, because the young duck-billed platypus has rudimentary teeth resembling those of multituberculates. At present there is no direct evidence of an evolutionary connection, however, as the interval between the last multituberculates and the first known monotremes is about thirty-six million years (Eocene to Pleistocene).

Symmetrodonts were mammals whose upper molars had three cusps arranged symmetrically in the form of a triangle, with the apical (and largest) cusp on the lingual side. They seem to have lived only in the Jurassic period and it is not certain whether they died out without leaving any descendants, or whether they are phylogenetically related to the trituberculates, another group of mammals.

The molars of trituberculates (pantotheria) had three cusps, varying in arrangement, and the dentition of these animals in general resembled the modern carnivore type. The members of the group were of different shapes and sizes. They lived during the Jurassic and early Cretaceous periods and are regarded as the basic group from which marsupials and placental mammals sprang.

The docodonts, a heterogenous and very distinctive group, so far known only from late Triassic and Jurassic strata, may have followed on after the trituberculates; their teeth were characterized by two cusps. The docodonts may possibly have been an evolutionally blind alley.

The only Jurassic mammals to continue into the Cretaceous period were multituberculates and pantotheria. Trituberculates (pantotheria) gave rise to two still extant groups—marsupials and placental mammals. They were small animals and we know very little about them. Their remains have been found over a wide area (England, North America, Mongolia), but the number of large skeletal units is negligible. At first there were more marsupials than placental mammals and their peak period was the late Cretaceous, when they inhabited all the then existent continents, except Africa. In the Tertiary era, when placental mammals began to flourish, the marsupials were unable to compete with them and survived only in geographically isolated regions. *Didelphis,* a genus related to present-day opossums, was distributed all over the world. Its European members died out in the early Miocene, but in North America it has survived down to the present, with only minor changes, and it represents the maximum phylogenetic resistance ever to be observed among mammals.

In Australia and South America, marsupials produced a number of forms resembling placental mammals. Large predators evolved alongside herbivorous types. We have an interesting case of evolutionary convergence in the South American *Thylacosmilus* (Plate 95, pp. 236—7), which looked like the early Tertiary sabre-toothed cats (machairodontids) of Europe and America.

Placental mammals were represented in the Cretaceous period by insectivores (Plate 75, p. 197), small mammals which even today retain ancient characters in, for example, tooth structure and brain development.

The Palaeocene, the first period of the Cainozoic era, is sometimes described as the 'prologue to the evolution of the mammals' (meaning mainly placental mammals akin to the Recent fauna). Two large groups of mammals—creodonts and condylarths—became prominent. Creodonts (Plates 76—78, pp. 198—202) evidently evolved from late Cretaceous flesh-eating insectivores. They were characterized by tapering jaws and unreduced dentition. Their teeth were constructed similarly to these of canids, except that the carnassials developed from the second molars and not from the first. Creodonts were predators; they were not the ancestors of present-day carnivores, however, but were a separate branch which evolved in a different direction from them. Condylarthra (Plate 81, p. 209) can be said to be the first ungulates. They did not differ much from creodonts and today the two are usually grouped together. They were omnivorous and herbivorous and their limbs looked like those of canids rather than of ungulates.

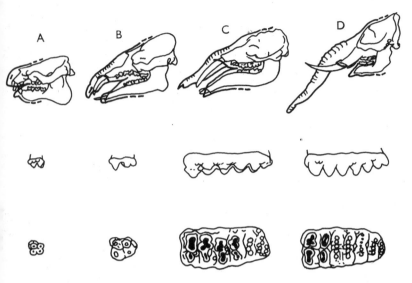

Fig. 5. Evolution of elephants
  A. *Moeritherium* (Eocene)
  B. *Palaeomastodon* (Oligocene — not described in this book)
  C. *Gomphotherium* (Miocene)
  D. *Stegolophodon* (Pliocene — not described in this book)
  E. *Archidiscodon* (Pleistocene)
  F. Mammoth (late Pleistocene)

Proboscideans B to D belong to mastodons, E and F to true elephants.

During the Eocene, mammals underwent some degree of 'modernization'. Bats, prosimians and rodents evolved from insectivores and the first true carnivores appeared. The first of the latter were the miacids, primitive beasts of prey rather like civet-cats in appearance. They could hardly have been descended from creodonts, as they lived contemporaneously with them, but they may have evolved by a separate route from late Cretaceous insectivores. The true carnivores are presumed to have evolved polyphyletically, i.e. in several simultaneous, parallel lines, from the outset. Representatives of Recent families are already encountered in the Oligocene (Plates 79 and 80, pp. 205, 207).

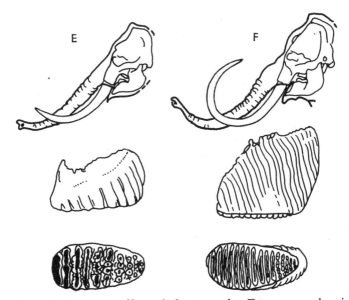

Ungulates were affected the most by Eocene modernization. The first odd- and even-toed ungulates evolved (the former from Condylarthra, perhaps, the latter from still unknown ancestors). As the evolution of odd-toed ungulates progressed, the number of digits diminished and, with the transition from the forest to the open country, new, more lightly built and agile forms appeared. Horses also began to evolve (Plates 82 and 83, pp. 211, 213). Rhinoceroses also evolved (Plate 84, p. 214), some of them parallel with primitive horses (Plate 87, p. 221). Even-toed ungulates were represented by primitive, heavy (Plate 85, p. 217) or moderately heavy forms (Plate 86, p. 218).

The evolution of proboscideans likewise started during the Eocene, when they were represented only by *Moeritherium* (Plate 93, p. 232). At the same time, mammals invaded what was for them a new environment—water. The first forms of cetaceans, which evolved from primitive carnivores, appeared (Plate 94, p. 234). They looked rather like the Cretaceous mosasaurs, and they were still very remote from dolphins and whales. Big faunal migrations occurred during the Oligocene and further forms evolved, mainly among the odd-toed ungulates. It is interesting to note the evolution of 'heavy' forms among other ungulate groups—often confined to the early Tertiary—as well as among odd-toed ungulates (Plates 88—92, pp. 222—230).

Mammals acquire their present form

The late Tertiary, in general, and the Miocene, in particular, were times of important changes. Some early Tertiary mammal groups disappeared and groups which occupy an important place among the present-day fauna stepped into the foreground. The main ones were odd- and even-toed ungulates, true carnivores and primates (monkeys). Tapirs (Plate 102, pp. 250—251), which had flourished in the Oligocene and had persisted into the late Tertiary, still held their ground. New, large forms included the rhinoceroses. Smaller types gradually disappeared and were replaced by large ones, the majority of which were still hornless, but were sometimes interestingly adapted (Plate 103, p. 253). Proboscideans, whose evolution began with tapir-like types, likewise produced large forms. Their incisors were progressively transformed into tusks and Miocene forms had one pair in the upper and one in the lower jaw. The other teeth also altered and their number was reduced so severely that, in late forms, we find only one pair in either jaw. The teeth grew larger, however, and in the true elephants the number of dental walls increased to such an extent that the teeth underwent lamellization. At the same time, the nose and upper lip were converted into a trunk. The limbs grew longer, but because the flexible trunk was able to transfer food straight to the mouth, the neck remained the same length or even became shorter (Plate 104, p. 255). Some proboscideans, such as *Platybelodon* (Plate 106, p. 259), displayed interesting forms of specialization.

The evolution of horses proceeded apace (Plate 99, p.

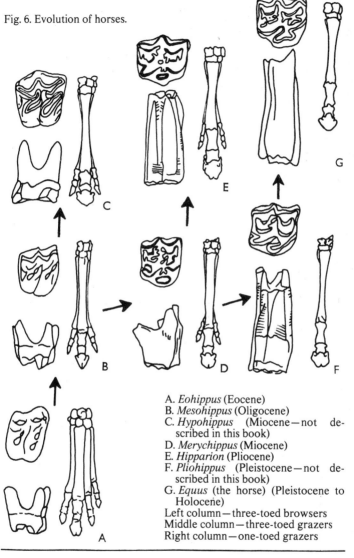

Fig. 6. Evolution of horses.

A. *Eohippus* (Eocene)
B. *Mesohippus* (Oligocene)
C. *Hypohippus* (Miocene — not described in this book)
D. *Merychippus* (Miocene)
E. *Hipparion* (Pliocene)
F. *Pliohippus* (Pleistocene — not described in this book)
G. *Equus* (the horse) (Pleistocene to Holocene)
Left column — three-toed browsers
Middle column — three-toed grazers
Right column — one-toed grazers

245). The number of toes was gradually reduced from five to three (tridactyly), the largest (middle) one carrying the whole weight of the body. Deer also continued to evolve during the Miocene (Plates 97 and 98, pp. 241, 243), but their forms were so far small and relatively primitive. Progress was likewise made by antelopes and giraffes, which looked more like unwieldy antelopes. Camels evolved alongside giraffes as another special group. Their initial forms looked more like deer or antelopes and their more advanced forms like llamas. The most widespread living species, the Arabian (one-humped) and the Bactrian (two-humped) camel, are extreme aberrant forms adapted to a life in the semi-desert or steppe, where they had no competitors. The giraffe-like *Alticamelus* (Plate 101, p. 249), which led the same type of life as present-day giraffes and is a further example of evolutionary convergence, was another highly specialized form.

Carnivores underwent large-scale radiation during the Miocene, new groups appearing among the primitive beasts of prey of the early Tertiary. Ursine carnivores evolved at the transition from the Oligocene to the Miocene. The first representatives, such as *Ursavus,* were about the size of a fox or a small dog. Their group very soon split up into several evolutionary lines, which broke away at different times. These lines evolved at different rates and to different degrees. In general, it can be claimed that ursids, during the Miocene, formed a heterogenous group of ancient types, all of which were omnivorous, but in many cases tended to be almost herbivorous (the Pleistocene cave bear for example). Forms about the size of a baribal are known only from the Pliocene and large bears from the Pleistocene. Several lines of hyenas also evolved during the Miocene, while among the felids, machairodontids, with their fangs undergoing rapid lengthening, became increasingly important.

On most of the continents (at least in the northern hemisphere), the climate grew drier and cooler during the Pliocene. The forests shifted to the mountains or equatorial regions, while the more temperate latitudes were transformed into almost endless grasslands of the same type as the African savanna. It was this expansion of the grasslands that made the Pliocene the 'golden age' of running mammals. The main animals involved were ungulates, which formed huge herds, and carnivores. The Miocene *Merychippus* evolved into the Pliocene *Hipparion* (Plate 100, p. 247), the characteristic animal of the Pliocene steppes. Various species of antelope and deer likewise became very widespread. In the giraffe family, forms like the Recent okapi and Recent African giraffes appeared. Pliocene giraffes occupied a much wider area than their present relative; for example, they are known from south European steppes (near Pikermi in Greece). Rhinoceroses now produced large forms which had horns on their nasal bones and were adapted to a steppe existence. Among the proboscideans, the mastodons attained the peak of their evolution (Plate 105, p. 256). They had two pairs of tusks, but the upper pair gradually predominated. The forest-dwelling deinotheres (Plate 107, p. 260) evolved along quite different lines. Large carnivores evolved alongside large ungulates. The main ones were the sabre-toothed machairodontids (Plate 96, p. 238), although large carnivores belonging to the true cats appeared as well.

The age of mammoths

The youngest era in the history of the Earth and of its life is known as the Quaternary. From the point of view of historical geology it is only the most recent part of the Cainozoic but there are two important factors which allow it to be evaluated as an independent geo-historical unit. One is the birth and development of human society, which has come to be an increasingly important factor influencing nature, and the other is the colder trend in the climate, especially in the northern hemisphere, where it had a very adverse effect on the existing phylogenetic development of organisms, and also caused marked discontinuity between the present-day fauna and flora and that of earlier geological periods, especially the early Tertiary.

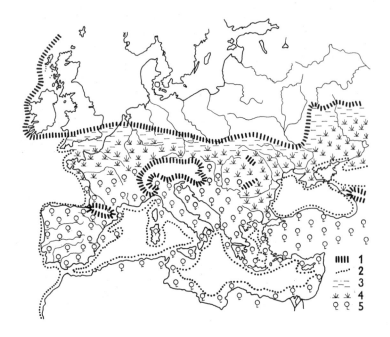

Fig. 7. Europe during the severest ice age (Mindel glacial).
1—limits of ice-sheets and glaciers
2—limits of dry land
3—tundra
4—cold loess steppe
5—forest

This cold trend is well-known as the ice ages (glacials) which characterized the Pleistocene, the first period of the Quaternary era. Although typical of the Pleistocene, glacials were not confined solely to this period. They are also known to have occurred in the Carboniferous period, in the later part of the Palaeozoic, 290 million years ago, when they mainly affected the southern hemisphere (what is now India, South Africa, Australia and Brazil). At the transition from the Proterozoic to the Palaeozoic, about 600 million years ago, practically the whole of the world was covered with ice and indications of this glaciation can be found in northern Europe, Siberia, China, Australia,

44

South Africa and North America. This glacial may have played a role in the great evolutionary turning-point known as the 'fossil records explosion'. Still earlier glacials have been demonstrated in the early Proterozoic (with at least two phases) and in the Archaeozoic (in South Africa).

Pleistocene cooling did not take place all at once. The climate had already started to become cooler and drier in the late Pliocene and the process culminated in the Pleistocene glaciogenic epoch. This was not a time of permanent cooling, however, but was composed of several glacials—cold periods which alternat rhythmically with warmer periods (interglacials). The glacials did not have a uniform temperature either, but were composed of periods of extreme cold, when Europe had an arctic type of climate, and milder periods, when the European climate was only a little colder than today and somewhat drier.

The climatic oscillations had a drastic effect on the fauna and flora. It was often so strong that it even influenced phylogenetic development. The original evolutionary trend was either accelerated by the oscillations of the climate, or, more often than not, it was retarded, inhibited or reversed by them. In regions where Pleistocene climatic oscillations had a less severe effect, in North Africa for example, the flora and fauna underwent only minor, and mostly phylogenetic, changes, so that evolutionary continuity from the Tertiary to the present day was maintained.

The beginning of the Pleistocene (also known as the Eopleistocene or Villafranchian period) was not very different from the last part of the Pliocene, so that some scientists put the division between them at 1.8 to 2 million years ago and others at 3, 3.2 or 3.5 million years ago. Despite a certain degree of cooling, the climate of the northern hemisphere was warmer than it is today. The cold waves were characterized by expansion of the forests and the warm, dry waves by ascendancy of the grasslands. At first, the fauna was not seriously affected by these oscillations. The Eopleistocene steppes and forests were inhabited by large mammals and still resembled the savannas of North Africa (the Serengeti for instance).

Among the typical Eopleistocene mammals which had survived from the late Tertiary we must include the mastodons (Plate 108, p. 262) and the rhinoceroses and tapirs. True elephants made their appearance for the first time, however (Plate 109, pp. 264—265). The three-toed *Hipparion* still existed at the beginning of the Pleistocene but it soon died out and was replaced by the one-toed *Allohippus*, which combined features of horses and zebras. Antelopes, typical animals of the Tertiary which still live in Africa, disappeared from the northern hemisphere at the beginning of the Pleistocene and their place was taken by deer. Carnivores were represented by the last of the 'sabre-toothed tigers' (Plate 122, p. 291), cheetahs and big cats of the genus *Panthera*.

The period known as the Glacipleistocene began about one million years ago. It was characterized by the development of true glacials, with expansion of the continental ice sheets and mountain glaciers. During the Günz glacial the ice did not advance very far, but in the more recent glacials the arctic ice sheets spread to central Europe and, in North America, to the region of the Great Lakes. The fauna of the northern hemisphere divided into the two types mentioned above, i. e. a 'warm' and a 'cold' fauna. *Palaeoloxodon antiquus* (Plate 110, p. 266) and the rhinoceroses *Dicerorhinus etruscus* and *D. kirchbergensis* (Plates 118 and 119, 283—285) are examples of 'warm' fauna, while an example of adaptation to a cold climate is to be found in the transformation of the warmth-loving elephant (Plate 109, pp. 264—265), via intermediate steppe-dwelling forms (Plates 112 and 113, pp. 270, 273), to the typical cold-loving woolly mammoth (Plate 114, p. 275). Rhinoceroses (Plates 120 and 121, pp. 287, 288) underwent similar adaptation. The mammoth faunas of the more recent glacials represent the peak of adaptation to a cold climate, when the reindeer (Plate 127, p. 301) joined the mammoth and the woolly rhinoceros as an arctic element

46

and the chamois and the ibex (Plate 126, p. 299) appeared as alpine elements. Carnivores were mainly represented by a well-known trio—the cave lion (Plate 123, p. 292), the cave bear (Plate 124, p. 294) and the cave hyena.

Despite its adaptation to the cold climate, the mammoth fauna died out. In the last glacial and during the Holocene postglacial it was replaced by a warmth-loving forest fauna which spread northwards from the south. The Holocene is also a period of maximum development of human society. In Europe, man did not appear on a large scale until the Eem interglacial and in North America not until the last glacial. Originally he formed part of the 'warm' fauna, but owing to his ability to adapt himself to environmental changes actively (by producing implements, weapons and clothing, etc.), as well as passively, at the end of the Pleistocene and the beginning of the Holocene he became the new dominant element in nature. Whereas the Pleistocene hunter was a part of the animal population, Holocene man interferes with natural processes and modifies them. The transformation of grasslands and forests to farmland radically altered conditions of life, particularly for large mammals, and directly affected animal associations, severely reducing the numbers of some species and wiping others out completely. On the other hand, man introduced and bred various types of domestic animals. Pleistocene man may be blameless as far as extinction of the Pleistocene fauna is concerned, but we cannot say the same about Holocene man.

In the following illustrations, the animals are described in the same order as they have been mentioned in the introduction and under the same headings as the various sections of the introduction. The abbreviations B.M., G.A., and G.D. denote the animal's body measurements, geological age (in years from the present) and geographical distribution;
cm = centimetres,   dm = decimetres,   m = metres,
km = kilometres.

Precambrian animals left few traces of their existence, partly because they did not possess calcareous or siliceous shells or hard-parts capable of fossilization, and partly because the geological processes of later geological periods completely destroyed the little that did remain of the Precambrian. This makes the few individual finds that there are all the more precious and finds of whole associations even more so. One of the latter comes from sandstone in the Ediacara Hills in south Australia, 450 kilometres to the north of Adelaide, where a rich association of organisms of a soft-bodied nature, without hard parts and mostly of previously unknown forms, was discovered.

The impressions of the bodies of jelly-fish-like creatures show that medusae are an ancient group which evolved long before the Cambrian period.

Spriggina was an animal about five centimetres long, with a narrow body and numerous lateral outgrowths. It is possible that trilobites evolved from some such form.

Dickinsonia was about half a metre long. Some authors classify it among the worms, others regard it as a coelenterate. Similar forms may have been of great significance for the evolution of bivalves and gastropods.

Tribrachidium was a curious animal most closely resembling an echinoderm. Its systematic classification and phylogenetic significance are still obscure.

Parvancorina is likewise a problematical and still unclassified fossil.

Rangea and *Charnia* were possibly coelenterates and related to the Recent sea-pens.

In addition to the animals illustrated here, hypothetical algae and sponges and a worm in a sand burrow have also been found.

G.A.: late Precambrian, over 600 million years
G.D.: south Australia

Lyssacina

The members of the order Lyssacina are sea sponges with a skeleton formed of siliceous spicules. They were already present in Cambrian seas and reached the peak of their evolution in the Mesozoic era. After that, their significance diminished but they still occur today. The spicules were loose, i.e. unconnected, and when the animal died they fell apart, so that the exact form of the body is not known; we can only assume that it was spherical or cylindrical. Large spicules on the distal part of the body formed a kind of 'tail', anchoring the sponge in the ooze (certain Recent related sea sponges have similar spicules). Extant members of the *Lyssacina* live in cold, deep-sea water, but Cambrian members seem to have lived in shallow littoral water illuminated and warmed by the sun, to a depth of 200 metres. Some species occurred en masse and formed peculiar communities (bioherms) similar to coral reefs. As a rule, only the separate spicules have been preserved and the rocks are sometimes full of them.

B.M.: not definitely known
G.A.: Cambrian, 550 million years
G.D.: Europe, North America

Medusae

Medusae are free-swimming soft-bodied invertebrates whose body disc—the umbrella—may resemble a domed bell or a shallow dish. The diameter of the umbrella can vary from a few centimetres to two metres. A short oral cone, terminating in most medusae in a mouth, dangles from the centre of the under side of the umbrella. The edges of the mouth are fringed with lobes or arms. The mouth leads to a gastric cavity, which is partitioned off into a central stomach and four gastrovascular pouches. Medusae live mostly in salt water. Their body is composed of a gelatinous substance and contains 99% water, so that their chances of fossilization are obviously very small. The umbrellas have thus been preserved only as impressions. Natural casts of the alimentary cavities, forming very interesting stud-like or stellate structures, are more frequent. Finds of whole fossilized individuals are rare in the extreme and fossil medusae can therefore be only approximately reconstructed. In the picture, the medusa on the left could belong to the genus *Brooksella* and the one on the right to the genus *Protolyella*.

B.M.: umbrella diameter 10—40 cm
G.A.: middle Cambrian, 550 million years
G.D.: central Europe

Paradoxides gracilis Boeck (foreground)

This moderately large trilobite with a semicircular head had free cheeks, each with a long, narrow, recurved spine, and relatively large eyes. Its elongated trunk was composed of twenty segments, and again was adorned with longish, recurved lateral spines. Its pygidium (caudal shield) was comparatively small and had one or two pairs of long spines on the posterior margin. *Paradoxides* was a typical trilobite of the 'Atlantic' Cambrian sea which covered Europe and the eastern part of North America. Developmental stages of this genus are also known.

B.M.: total length 14 cm
G.A.: middle Cambrian, 540 million years
G.D.: central Europe

Ellipsocephalus hoffi Schlotheim (centre)

This very characteristic trilobite of Cambrian seas had a semicircular head, narrow free cheeks without appendages and large eyes. The thorax was composed of twelve segments and the pygidium was small. This tiny, but rather pretty trilobite lived in the ooze on the seabed.

B.M.: total length 2—3 cm
G.A.: middle Cambrian, 540 million years
G.D.: central Europe

The sponges in the background belong to the genus *Protospongia*. They had a very simple body structure and the details on sea sponges given in description to Plate 2 apply to them also.

Conocoryphe sulzeri Schlotheim (on right)

Conocoryphe was a trilobite with a semicircular head and a conical glabella (the middle part of the head shield). The head shield was extended posteriorly into moderately long, blunt-tipped spines. Eyes were absent, the animal thus being blind. The thorax had fourteen segments and the rounded pygidium six to eight segments. *Conocoryphe* was common in the middle Cambrian and does not seem to have had any special preference as regards its benthic habitat.

B.M.: total length 8 cm
G.A.: middle Cambrian, 540 million years
G.D.: Europe

Ptychoparia striata Emmrich

(two individuals on left)

While resembling *Conocoryphe,* this species was small and had distinct eyes. The thorax was composed of fourteen segments, as in *Conocoryphe,* and the pygidium was quite large. *Ptychoparia* evidently preferred a sandy substrate.

B.M.: total length 6 cm
G.A.: middle Cambrian, 540 million years
G.D.: Europe

Marrolithus ornatus Sternberg   (left foreground)

Marrolithus was a characteristic Ordovician trilobite. Its bulging glabella and cheeks had a typically perforated horseshoe border, tapering off into recurved spines longer than the animal's body. The thorax was short and the pygidium small; when in danger, the animal could tuck its body and tail under its head shield. *Marrolithus* was very common, as seen from the quantity of shield fragments found in some Ordovician sediments.
B.M.: total length 2 cm
G.A.: late Ordovician, 450 million years
G.D.: Europe (Czechoslovakia)

Aristocystites bohemicus Barrande   (top right)

The ovoid or pear-shaped test of this Palaeozoic cystoid (a type of echinoderm) was composed of a large number (150—200) of platelets. At the apex of the theca there was a mouth, an anal opening (covered by a valvular pyramid composed of numerous triangular plates) and two arms. It was stalkless and sessile, and was anchored directly to the substrate by its posterior end.
B.M.: length of test 6 cm
G.A.: late Ordovician, 450 million years
G.D.: Europe (Czechoslovakia)

Aegiromena aquila Barrande   (right foreground)

This brachiopod had a tiny, thin-walled shell with a flat dorsal valve and a convex ventral valve. Both parts had radial grooves and ridges.
B.M.: width of shell 2 cm
G.A.: late Ordovician, 450 million years
G.D.: Europe (Czechoslovakia)
   A swimming orthoceratid (cephalopod) can be seen near the top of the picture (see Plate 8).

Corals

Corals were common in early Palaeozoic seas, their remains providing the basic material from which numerous types of limestone were later formed.

Favosites tachlowitzensis Počta (centre)

This very widespread type of coral formed large honeycomb colonies composed of minute, thin-walled and usually hexagonal corallites two to two and a half millimetres in diameter. *Favosites* was common in central Bohemia, on the island of Gotland (Sweden), in Estonia and in various other places in Europe.

Entelophyllum prosperum Počta (centre foreground)

This solitary (non-colony-forming) type of coral had a cylindrical or conical theca with a strongly ribbed, grooved and furrowed surface.

Omphyma grandis Počta (right foreground)

Although similar to the preceding species, the corallite of *Omphyma grandis* was shaped like a wide cone and had root-like processes (not visible in the picture) at its base to anchor it to the seabed.

B.M.: about 20 cm (all three species)
G.A.: late Silurian, 410 million years
G.D.: central Europe

Orthoceratids

Orthoceratids were cephalopods related to the
present-day *Nautilus.* In certain localities early
Palaeozoic limestones are full of shells of these
creatures. They are divided into several chambers
separated from each other by partitions, their
surface being 'decorated' with ribs, nodes and
spines, and in a few rare cases the remains of
colouring can be detected. The first chamber behind the opening contained the 'body' of the
animal, the others were filled with gas which kept
the shell buoyant and made it possible for the
animal to swim. Only the animal's head and tentacles protruded from the shell. When in danger,
Orthoceras, an Ordovician cephalopod with
a straight shell, could withdraw into its shell and
even close the shell with a 'lid'. Orthoceratids un-
doubtedly lived at the bottom of the sea. Most of
them were probably poor swimmers and floated
above the seabed or crawled about on it, with the
mouth of their dwelling-chamber facing down-
ward. Like octopuses, they were predators. In
their acme they had no rivals, but in the late Palaeozoic new groups (mainly vertebrates), with
which the orthoceratids were unable to compete,
appeared.

B.M.: length of shell a few dm to 1 m
G.A.: late Silurian, 410 million years
G.D.: central Europe

Scyphocrinites excavatus Schlotheim

This sea-lily was the largest and commonest of the Bohemian crinoids. It had a large, domed and somewhat elongated dorsal cup (calyx). The slightly bulging plates of the calyx were all firmly joined together and had a finely ribbed or granular surface. The arms were very well developed; below the upper margin of the calyx they divided into two secondary branches, which further bifurcated until they terminated in feathery rows of finely segmented, terminal appendages. As a rule, only the proximal parts of the arms have been preserved. The stalk was very long and was composed of a large number of button-like columnals with a single, central, five-pointed opening. At the base, the stalk terminated in a lobolith, a special apparatus shaped like a hollow

sphere and divided into four to six chambers, whose purpose was to hold the animal on the substrate. In some localities, rocks are full of segments of the stalks, which form crinoid-limestones showing that *Scyphocrinites* once flourished in Silurian seas. (In the foreground we can see the tabulate coral *Favosites tachlowitzensis* Počta and the solitary coral *Chonophylum grandis* Edwards et Haime).

B.M.: length of dorsal cup 10 cm
    width of dorsal cup 9 cm
G.A.: late Silurian, 410 million years
G.D.: central Europe (Bohemia)

Heterostraci

The Heterostraci were primitive fish-like vertebrates with a dorsal and ventral shield over their head and the anterior part of their body. Because of these they are often described as 'armoured fishes', but they were not fishes in the true meaning of the term. Their armour was wide and flat on the back, the eyes were localized on the dorsal aspect and in the ventral shield there was a jawless mouth. The gill apparatus was contained in a special cavity, the gill-chamber. The mobile posterior part of the body was covered with hard dentine scales. The picture shows three species of these vertebrates.

Pteraspis rostrata Agassiz (at the top) had a peculiar dorsal shield which tapered off into a kind of a beak at the front and into a spine at the back. The mouth lay below the beak.

The armour of *Psammolepis paradoxa* Agassiz (in the middle) was composed of large plates on which there were nodulous outgrowths.

Drepanaspis gemuendensis Schüter (at the bottom) was armed with large plates separated by scale-covered areas.

B.M.: length of body about 20 cm (all three species)
G.A.: early and middle Devonian, 370 million years
G.D.: Europe

Placodermi

The remains of these bizarre, primitive, jawed fishes were once thought to be the remains of crustaceans, insects or testudinates. The common feature of this group is the thick armour which covered the anterior part of the body. The skeleton was mainly cartilaginous. The pectoral fins, or to be more exact the fore limbs, were likewise encased in armour, which was segmented as in crustaceans' legs. There are a great many opinions as to the function of such limbs, but the most feasible one seems to be that the placoderms used them for pushing off from the seabed, since their heavy armour must have made swimming very difficult for them.

The armour of *Pterichthys* (above) was convex and was composed of large plates; the rest of the body was covered with round scales. The thoracic (fore) limbs were shorter than the body armour. In *Bothriolepis canadensis* Whiteaves (below), the armour was flatter and the posterior part of the body was probably bare and scaleless.

B.M.: body length about 20 cm (both species)
G.A.: early Devonian, 380 million years
G.D.: *Pterichthys* — western Europe
   Bothriolepis — North America (Canada)

Acanthodians

Acanthodians were the earliest jawed fishes. In form they resembled sharks, but their epidermis was covered with tiny rhomboid platelets like the scales of holosteans (gars, bowfins). According to the latest views, acanthodians were an independent phylogenetic branch of fishes which evolved, perhaps at the beginning of the Devonian period, from little-specialized forms close to Recent chondrosteans. Acanthodians did, in fact, have a cartilaginous skeleton, but their fins had a wide, bony base and were reinforced on their anterior margin with a dentine spine. Acanthodians lived in fresh water. Two genera are illustrated in the picture. In *Climatius* (below), the gill-slit was covered by an operculum. The lower jaw was toothed, the body flat-sided and relatively deep and between the pelvic and abdominal fins there were several pairs of free spines corresponding to further (rudimentary) paired fins. *Parexus* (above) resembled *Climatius*. In front of its dorsal fin it had a huge spine with two rows of teeth.

B.M.: total length — *Climatius* 7 — 8 cm
Parexus 12 cm
G.A.: early Devonian, 380 million years
G.D.: Europe

Xenacanthus decheni Goldfuss

Xenacanthus was a primitive freshwater shark. Its cartilaginous skeleton was reinforced with calcified blocks, and its vertebral arches were completely ossified, but the skull was cartilaginous. The mouth was armed with large numbers of typical teeth, each with two large, diverging points and a smaller third point between them. Behind its head *Xenacanthus* had a large dentine spine with two rows of minute, file-like teeth posteriorly. The function of this spine, which seems to have been movable, has not yet been fully explained. The trunk was long and slender and the caudal part of the spinal column was not shortened as it is in bony fishes (teleosteans). The long dorsal fin began behind the head and stretched as far as the tail. One of the most interesting things about *Xenacanthus* is the structure of the pectoral fins,

which had a segmented middle axis round which the lateral rays were arranged in the manner of a palm-leaf. Among living fishes, this is found only in the Australian lung-fish. *Xenacanthus* inhabited muddy lakes and pools in swampy regions, where it hunted small fishes belonging to the genus *Amblypterus*.

B.M.: total length 50—70 cm
G.A.: late Carboniferous, 300 million years
G.D.: Europe

Meganeura monyi Brongniart

The dragon-fly *Meganeura monyi* was a veritable giant among the insects. It belonged to the long extinct order Meganisoptera, which formed an intermediate group between living dragon-flies and the Palaeodictyoptera, an extinct group of primitive winged insects. *Meganeura* had a large dragon-fly head and a primitively constructed thorax and limbs. Its large, richly veined wings could not be folded, even when the insect was at rest, and could be moved only up and down. *Meganeura* inhabited Carboniferous swamps and marshes, where many species of small, primitive insects were its prey. Its larval development, which took place in swamp water, was probably not very different from the early development of living dragon-flies.

B.M.: wing span 70 cm
G.A.: late Carboniferous,
      300 million years
G.D.: western and central Europe

Eusthenopteron foordi Whiteaves

This crossopterygian had an intricately constructed skull, covered with a shield of dermal bones. It had large, conical teeth in its jaws and in front of these, on the edge of the jaws, rows of very tiny teeth. Between its jawbone and its palatine bones there were nasal passages (choanas) enabling it to breathe air. It had a long, anteriorly flattened body covered with thin, rounded and overlapping scales. The paired fins had as their base a large shoulder and pelvic girdle, to which the thick bones of the actual limb were attached. The fin rays were parallel (not radial as in the majority of fishes) and thus formed the pattern for the deve-

lopment of the phalanges of the land animal. The limbs of *Eusthenopteron* could be used on the land as well as in the water, so that, although the creature normally lived in swamp water, if it became necessary it could use its fins to move from a pool which was drying up to one which still contained water. The American authors Gregory and Raven (1941) derived the amphibian limbs from the limb of *Eusthenopteron*, but according to the latest research *Eusthenopteron* was not an initial form of amphibian, but simply indicates the lines along which amphibians evolved.

B.M.: total length 28 cm
G.A.: late Devonian, 360 million years
G.D.: North America

Ichthyostega species

Ichthyostega, the first terrestrial four-legged animal, had a fish-like body, but well developed limbs. Its mixture of piscine and amphibian characters makes it an important link in the evolution of amphibians from fishes. Its skull was wider than it was long and was structurally reminiscent of the skull of crossopterygians. Sharp-pointed, conical teeth, typical of stegocephalians, were present in its jaws and on its palate. Its most important feature, however, was the separation of the skull from the shoulder girdle with the formation of a cervical spinal region. This provided the head with freedom of movement—a very important factor for the terrestrial vertebrate, for which the twisting and turning of the whole body, normal in fishes, was very difficult and most impractical. Another important advance was the development of the shoulder and pelvic girdle, as supports for limb movement. The long, thick tail had a caudal fin and the caudal vertebrae were of a fully piscine character. *Ichthyostega* inhabited fresh-water pools and small lakes and spent little of its time on the dry land. The details of its biology and ecology, and even its taxonomy (specification into species) have yet to be established.

B.M.: total length 95 cm
G.A.: late Devonian, 350 million years
G.D.: Greenland

Diplovertebron punctatum Fritsch

Diplovertebron was a stegocephalian with a somewhat 'reptilian' body. Its skull in particular, produced into a tapering triangle, was like a small-scale replica of a crocodile's skull. The otic notches in the posterior part of the skull, which are normally present in primitive amphibians, were very small in *Diploverte-bron*, but the structure of the vertebrae was very primitive and the notochord persisted into adulthood. The limbs were sturdy, but lightly built and had five digits. The carpal or 'wrist' and tarsal or 'ankle' bones were cartilaginous and did not ossify. The limbs were used mainly in the water, where hydrostatic pressure reduced the weight of the body. *Diplovertebron punctatum* inhabited European Carboniferous swamps, where it caught fish and smaller amphibians. Another, closely related species lived in the Pennsylvanian period in North America. *Diplovertebron* is an important link in evolution, because its body structure resembled that of a reptile.

B.M.: total length 60 cm
G.A.: late Carboniferous, 300 million years
G.D.: central Europe

Discosauriscus pulcherrimus Fritsch

Discosauriscus was an amphibian with a lizard- or salamander-like body. It had a wide skull with deep otic notches and large eye sockets and its nostrils were right at the tip of its snout. Its relatively slim body was covered with small, round scales. Growth stages, once described as separate species, are also known. In the early stages of its development the animal breathed by means of gills and its skeleton was not yet ossified (or only in part). In the later stages the skeleton gradually ossified and the gills disappeared as their function of respiration was taken over by the lungs. *Discosauriscus* evidently lived in clean, well-aerated water. It inhabited shallow pools in swamps thickly overgrown with vegetation, where it sought both shelter and the insects, insect larvae, small fish and the young of other stegocephalians which formed its staple diet. It is interesting to note that individuals measuring less than forty centimetres lived in the water, while skulls up to five centimetres long are known from dry land sediments. It looks as though old individuals left the water and took completely to the dry land. The picture also shows a young *Discosauriscus* (bottom right) and the related stegocephalian *Letoverpeton moravicus* Fritsch (bottom left).

B.M.: total length 40 cm (?)
G.A.: early Permian, 280 million years
G.D.: central Europe (Czechoslovakia)

Chelyderpeton germanicus Kühn

This lizard-like amphibian had an elongated, tri-angular head with a rounded snout. The length of the skull seems to have depended on age; the skull of young individuals was short and round and with advancing age it grew longer. The jaws were armed with twenty-five to thirty narrow, relatively long and partly recurved teeth. The elongated body probably terminated in a flat-sided tail, adapted for swimming. The limbs were short and each had five digits, the middle one being the longest. They were rather puny and were evidently better suited to movement in the water than on the land. The skin was scaleless except on the abdominal part of the body, where it was covered with an armour composed of small platelets arranged in diagonal rows. *Chely-derpeton* was an amphibian that inhabited lakes and pools, shallow rather than deep water. It was a predator that hunted smaller stegocephalians. Its position in its own animal community was similar to that of present-day crocodiles.

B.M.: body length 1.2 m
G.A.: early Permian, 280 million years
G.D.: central Europe

Diadectes phaseolinus Cope (above)

This heavily built reptile was a typical member of the cotylo-saur group. Seen from above, its skull was triangular, with a rounded snout. The parietal region was flat. The peg-like teeth were longer in the front of the snout and protruded outwards. The short, massive limbs had five, flat-clawed toes. One of the first terrestrial vertebrates, *Diadectes* was clearly herbivorous.

B.M.: total length 1.8 to 2.3 m
G.A.: early Permian, 260 million years
G.D.: North America (Texas)

Seymouria baylorensis Broili (below)

As a relatively primitive four-footed animal resembling both ste-gocephalians and primitive reptiles, *Seymouria* has often been discussed in the literature. It had an elongated head and a round-tipped snout. The structure of its skull and sharp-pointed teeth, which were present on the palatine bones as well as in the jaws, was of the amphibian type (in some respects it is actually reminis-cent of *Ichthyostega*), but the structure of the spine and the limbs was of the reptilian type and brings to mind members of the cotylosaur group. Nothing is known about the embryonic deve-lopment of *Seymouria*. Today *Seymouria* is usually ranked among the amphibians; at one time it was considered to be a di-rect ancestor of the reptiles, but its geological age makes this impossible (reptiles are already known from the Carboniferous period). It may be an aberrant amphibian branch whose evolu-tion stopped at a stage when it closely resembled the forebears of the reptiles.

B.M.: total length 70 cm
G.A.: early Permian, 260 million years
G.D.: North America (Texas)

Edaphosaurus pogonias Cope

This well-known, fearsome-looking reptile belongs to the pely-cosaur group. The long spines on its cervical and dorsal verte-brae had lateral outgrowths between which a leathery border was spanned during the animal's lifetime. This imposing appara-tus was most probably not a defence weapon, but its purpose was probably to keep the animal cool by fanning it. Despite its ap-pearance, *Edaphosaurus* was a harmless vegetarian.

B.M.: total length 3—4 m
G.A.: early Permian, 260 million years
G.D.: North America (Texas)

Dimetrodon incisivus Cope   (above) 22 →

This very interesting and odd-looking reptile was a pelycosaur. Its high-vaulted skull was forty-five centimetres long. Its jaws were armed with sharp and partly differentiated teeth, in the front there were one or two pairs of pseudocanines. The cervical, caudal and the dorsal vertebrae had extremely long spines which probably had skin stretched between them, again probably used to cool the owner. *Dimetrodon's* dentition indicates that it was a predator which hunted smaller reptiles and amphibians.

B.M.: total length 2—3 m
G.A.: early Permian, 260 million years
G.D.: North America (Oklahoma, Texas)

Varanosaurus acutirostris Broili   (below)

Despite its name, this animal belongs to the lizard-like pelyco-saurs and is not related to the monitor lizards. It had a flattened, elongated skull and a pointed snout with a row of sharp teeth, including two pairs of conspicuous pseudocanines. It was a small, nimble reptile, shown by its dentition to have been a predator.

B.M.: total length up to 1 m
G.A.: early Permian, 260 million years
G.D.: North America (Texas)

Scutosaurus
karpinskii Hartmann-Weinberg

This large, unwieldy and ungainly animal still resembled amphibians (advanced stegocephalians) in many respects. It is one of the primitive reptiles of the cotylosaur group. *Scutosaurus* had a wide skull with peculiar outgrowths. Behind its nostrils, at the corner of its mouth, there was yet another small, horny process. Like stegocephalians, it possessed a parietal eye. The angle of the lower jaw was remarkably massive. In each jaw there were fifteen or sixteen flat teeth whose crowns were divided into nine to seventeen cusps. The robust trunk was covered with spiked armour. The tail was short and the stumpy limbs had large, blunt claws. *Scutosaurus* was evidently a terrestrial animal which lived beside water or in marshy or swampy regions. The genus apparently died out at the same time as other groups of primitive cotylosaurs (the South African pareiasaurs for instance), at the end of the Permian period.

B.M.: total length 3 m
       height of body 1.3 m
G.A.: late Permian, 250 million years
G.D.: north-eastern Europe

Sauroctonus
progressus Hartmann-Weinberg

Sauroctonus was a moderately large, carnivorous reptile. Its flattened, triangular skull was about twenty-five centimetres long, with a parietal eye, a primitive character, on the crown. The upper and lower jaw each contained one pair of massive canines (the upper pair was the larger); the other teeth were smaller, but were also sharp and pointed. In addition, minute, blunt teeth were present on the palatine bones. The lower jaw was widened to form a kind of chin. The long, lightly built, five-toed limbs bore a resemblance to mammals' limbs, but despite its 'mammalian' characters *Sauroctonus* was not one of the ancestors of the mammals.

B. M.: total length about 3 m
G. A.: late Permian, 250 million years
G. D.: eastern Europe (Volga basin)

Mesosaurus tenuidens Gervais

Mesosaurus is one of the oldest known aquatic reptiles, and although thoroughly adapted to life in the water, it could still move on the dry land. It had a long, tapering snout with many large, long teeth which acted as a 'fishing-net'. Its nostrils were situated close to its eyes — a common feature in aquatic reptiles and mammals. As an adaptation to movement in water its limbs had diminished in size. They terminated in five digits joined together by webbing. The fore limbs were somewhat shorter and thinner than the hind limbs—a relic of the mesosaurs' terrestrial origin. Mesosaurs inhabited inland seas, where they lived mainly on fish. It is possible that they spent short periods on the land, to lay their eggs for instance. Phylogenetically they are a very interesting group. They display certain signs of kinship to the ichthyosaurs, although it is not certain whether they were actually their ancestors. They also appear to bear some relationship to the cotylosaurs and possibly to the pelycosaurs. The mesosaurs are of great significance to palaeogeography: related species occur in southern Africa, South America and Gondwana (central India), demonstrating that these continents were at one time united.

B. M.: total length 70 cm
G. A.: early Permian, 280 million years
G. D.: southern Africa

Placodus gigas Agassiz

Placodus was a comparatively slender reptile with a short neck, a long tail and a triangular, high-backed body. It had a massive skull with a relatively wide snout. In the upper jaw there were four, and in the lower jaw three, pairs of stud-like teeth one centimeter in diameter, with a thick layer of enamel and no cusps. Before the animals' anatomy was known, they were regarded as fishes' teeth. Similar smaller teeth were present on the palatine bones. Chisel-like incisors protruded from the anterior margin of the snout. The parietal eye on top of the head assisted the animal with orientation rather than its vision and its presence is regarded as quite a primitive characteristics. The vertebral processes of *Placodus* dove-tailed into each other and were firmly connected, so that the trunk was rigid. The abdomen was covered with a special armour formed of the bent, right-angled abdominal ribs. The fore and hind limbs were both well-developed. *Placodus* evidently lived beside the sea. It was actually a terrestrial animal, but ventured to the sea in search of food. Molluscs, brachiopods, crustaceans and other inhabitants of the seabed formed its staple diet: it was able to crush their shells with its blunt teeth. Its long, flat-sided tail was its main aid in underwater swimming.

B.M.: total length 2.5 m
G.A.: middle Triassic, 210 million years
G.D.: Europe

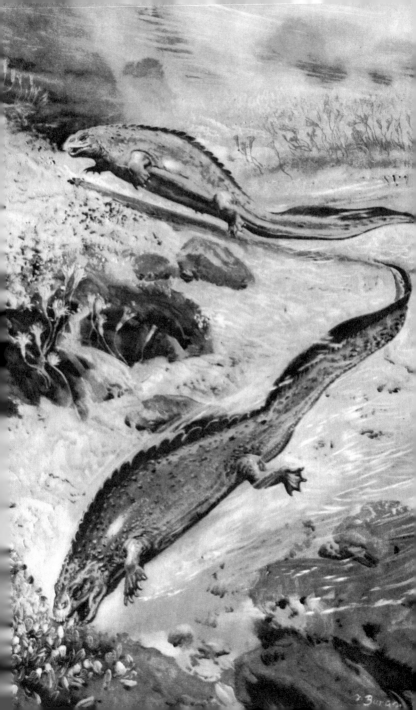

Henodus chelyops v. Huene

Henodus is a very curious reptile. Despite its appearance it was not a testudinate, but belonged to the placodonts (see *Placodus* Pl. 26). It had a square, long-backed head with a fore-shortened facial part and a wide, toothless, sharp-edged snout. Its short body was encased in a turtle-like shell. The under side of the shell was formed of the abdominal ribs and the dorsal part was composed of bony, dermal plates; the sides spread out like wings. The limbs were small and puny, but they nevertheless allowed some form of movement on the dry land, which was no doubt necessary when the eggs had to be laid. Otherwise *Henodus* is thought to have lived entirely in the water. It inhabited lagoons and lakes and lived on shellfish and other small creatures.

B.M.: total length 0.7 to 1 m
G.A.: middle Triassic, 210 million years
G.D.: central Europe

Mixosaurus carnalius Bassani

Mixosaurus was the most primitive of the ichthyosaurs, or 'fish-lizards', and possessed many characters not encountered in later ichthyosaurs. Its round head tapered off into the beak-like jaws typical of ichthyosaurs, but they were shorter than in later forms. The back teeth were blunt and adapted for crushing the shells of marine animals. The caudal fin was long and narrow and was less fish-like than in later forms. The limbs were already converted to paddles, but the fore limbs had evolved further than the hind limbs. The humerus, radius and ulna of the fore limb and the femur, tibia and fibula of the hind limb were morphologically normally developed, whereas in later species they were transformed to tiny polygonal bones or to rounded structures not unlike carpal and tarsal bones. Like the Jurassic ichthyosaurs, *Mixosaurus* inhabited the open sea, where it lived on fish, cephalopods and other animals. *Mixosaurus* seems to have been viviparous (live-bearing), again like the Jurassic ichthyosaurs.

B.M.: total length 1—2 m
G.A.: middle Triassic, 210 million years
G.D.: Europe

Nothosaurus procerus Schröder

Nothosaurus was a relatively common, moderately large, early Triassic reptile. In many respects its body structure resembled that of the much later plesiosaurs, but it did not attain the plesiosaurs' high degree of adaptation to an aquatic environment, so that we cannot definitely claim that it was their ancestor. It had a narrow, elongated skull and a long neck. Its front teeth were very large in contrast to its much smaller back teeth. Its comparatively long and slender limbs were adapted for swimming, but had not yet been converted into paddles. The large front teeth, for piercing and holding prey, indicate that *Nothosaurus* lived on fish, but its limbs are indicative of an amphibious mode of life. A complete skeleton of the smaller species *Nothosaurus raabi* Schröder can be seen in the Natural History Museum in Berlin.

B.M.: total length 2—3 m
G.A.: early Triassic, 230 million years
G.D.: central Europe

Lystrosaurus murrayi Huxley

Lystrosaurus was one of the mammal-like reptiles. It was a comparatively small reptile with a round skull. Its nostrils were situated very high up, directly below the eye sockets. and its snout was converted into a turtle-like beak. A pair of long, fang-like teeth protruded from its upper jaw. It had a barrel-shaped body and relatively short, sturdy limbs. The fore limbs were more powerful than the hind limbs, and had five digits with large flat claws, which were probably adapted for digging. The mode of life of *Lystrosaurus* is a matter for dispute. The high nostrils seem to indicate that it was an aquatic animal, but the limbs were not adapted for swimming and not even the structure of the pelvis shows signs of habitual movement in the water. *Lystrosaurus* probably lived in the vicinity of water, or even more likely directly beside it, like today's hippopotamuses or, perhaps, beavers. It was a vegetarian and lived on aquatic plants, which it tore up with its fangs. Its powerful fore limbs were used either to scratch out the roots of aquatic plants or to dig a kind of lair. *Lystrosaurus* inhabited southern Africa and the latest finds of its bones in the Antarctic indicate that these two continents were once joined together and thus provide evidence in support of the continental drift theory.

B.M.: total length 80 cm
G.A.: early Triassic, 230 million years
G.D.: southern Africa, Antarctic

Saltoposuchus longipes v. Huene

This animal belongs to the extinct group of thecodonts, reptiles with a lizard-like body and a skeleton like a crocodile's in structure. Thecodonts had a relatively large skull which displayed many of the same characters as the skull of the primitive bird *Archaeopteryx*. Their fore limbs were short and their only function may have been to grasp food. Locomotion was achieved mainly by the hind limbs; these were well-developed and resembled avian hind limbs in many respects. *Saltoposuchus* moved primarily by running on the toes of its hind legs, using its extremely long tail to help it maintain its balance. Our knowledge of the mode of life of thecodonts is very small, but they seem to have lived in many different environments and not to have required a special type of diet. Phylogenetically they are a very important group. It is presumed that they gave rise to one evolutionary line leading to the birds, to another leading to the crocodiles and testudinates, and to a third leading to the gigantic dinosaurs of the Jurassic and Cretaceous periods.

B.M.: total length 87 cm
G.A.: late Triassic, 200 million years
G.D.: Europe

Triassochelys dux Jaeckel

The most primitive form of fossil testudinate, *Triassochelys,* was not yet able to withdraw its head and tail into its shell. A relatively well preserved skeleton found in Halberstadt near Trossingen (West Germany) can be seen in the Natural History Museum in Berlin. *Triassochelys* had massive armour formed of ossified plates. The width of the shell was greater than its length and the dorsal aspect was richly sculptured. The neck and tail were protected by dermal spikes. The skull grew to a length of twenty centimetres. The mouth was toothless and the front of the snout was compressed, forming a kind of beak. The most interesting primitive character shown by *Triassochelys* is the fact that the pelvic bones were not yet fused with the shell, as they are in later testudinates. The structure of the limbs and other morphological characters show that *Triassochelys* was a terrestrial animal and a vegetarian.

B.M.: body length 1 m
G.A.: late Triassic, 200 million years
G.D.: central Europe

Archelon ischyros Wieland

The Yale University museum possesses an almost complete skeleton and photographs of it appear in many palaeontological
publications. The head of the Yale specimen is sixty-four centimetres long, but an isolated skull found in southern Dakota
measured one metre. This makes *Archelon* the largest testudinate ever to have existed. It inhabited upper Cretaceous seas and
its virtually functionless carapace was reduced to a minimum. All
that was left of the plastron were four central plates (fonta-
nelles) with processes radiating in all directions. The limbs were
of the paddle type and the fore limbs were much larger than the
hind limbs, showing that *Archelon* was unlikely to have left the
water. Another thing which would have proved an obstacle if
these turtles had tried to set foot on the land was their considerable weight, since it is presumed that three-ton specimens were
by no means exceptional.

B.M.: total length 2—4 m
G.A.: late Cretaceous, 80 million years
G.D.: North America (Dakota)

Triadobatrachus massinoti Piveteau

This oldest known, primitive frog displays certain points of anatomical and phylogenetic kinship to stegocephalians. It was first
discovered in 1937, when Adrien Massinot, near the village of
Betsieka in northern Madagascar, found an almost complete skeleton. The animal must have been fossilized soon after its death,
because all the bones lay in their natural position. Only the anterior part of the skull and the ends of the limbs were missing.
Although it was found in marine deposits, the general structure
of *Triadobatrachus* shows that it may have lived for part of the
time on the land and breathed air. Its proximity to the mainland
is further borne out by the remains of terrestrial plants found
together with it. The skeleton found on Madagascar belonged to
a not quite adult individual and it therefore caused widespread
discussion in the scientific world. Recent studies have shown that
Triadobatrachus was in all probability an aberrant branch of the
phylogenetic line leading to modern types of frog.

B.M.: total length about 10 cm
G.A.: early Triassic, 220 million years
G.D.: Madagascar

Mastodonsaurus giganteus Jaeger

Mastodonsaurus was a giant among the stegocephalians and the largest animal of its time. Its size has never been surpassed by any other amphibian. It looked like a huge frog, but instead of being semicircular, as in frogs, its head was triangular and reached one and a quarter metres in length. The large, oval eye sockets were midway along the skull. The jaws were armed with conical teeth. The body was relatively small in proportion to the large head, and the tail was very short. The greatly reduced and puny limbs had cartilaginous carpal and tarsal joints. The marked reduction of the limbs and the sinus lines (an organ for orientation in the water) on the head show that *Mastodonsaurus* was an aquatic animal which hardly ever left the water. It inhabited swampy pools and lived mainly on fish, whose remains

have been found in its fossilized excreta (coprolites). According to some scientists, *Mastodonsaurus* was completely unable to leave the water, and this opinion is borne out by finds of large quantities of bones showing that in times of drought, when the pools dried up, these creatures died en masse. *Mastodonsaurus* was once thought to be responsible for the footprints found in Triassic sandstones and described as *'Chirotherium',* but more recent research has found that the tracks belong to lizard-like reptiles of the Pseudosuchia group.

B.M.: body length 3 m
G.A.: late Triassic, 200 million years
G.D.: central Europe

Brontosaurus excelsus Marsh

Brontosaurus, the 'thunder-lizard', is unquestionably the best-known Mesozoic reptile. It had a small skull, with small nostrils facing forwards and a small brain-pan. Despite its enormous size, *Brontosaurus* had the relatively smallest brain of all vertebrates. Consequently, like *Diplodocus*, it developed a second nerve centre in the lumbar region. It had a long, curved neck and as the cervical vertebrae approached the trunk, they became progressively longer and wider. Except for those in the tail region, the vertebrae were all large, but hollow. In view of the size of the body, this resulted in some reduction of body weight. *Brontosaurus* had limbs like pillars and the fore legs were somewhat shorter than the hind legs. Its tiny spatulate and peg-like teeth show that it was herbivorous and lived on aquatic plants. Some scien-

tists believe that *Brontosaurus* lived mostly in water, in lakes or in riverside pools, where it not only looked for food, but sought protection from predacious reptiles, against which it was defenceless. The water would also have taken some of the weight of its body off its limbs and enabled it to move freely about. It probably came out on to the dry land only to lay its eggs, although some scientists believe that it was viviparous and that the young were born in the water. Other scientists believe that the animal was, in fact, quite capable of living on dry land without needing the 'support' of water.

B.M.: total length 15 m
       height in lumbar region 5 m
G.A.: late Jurassic, 150 million years
G.D.: North America (Wyoming)

Diplodocus carnegii Hatcher

Diplodocus was the longest of the dinosaurs. Its body tapered off into an extremely long tail with a whip-like tip. Its relatively small head was borne on a long, S-shaped neck. It had pillar-like limbs and the fore legs were shorter than the hind legs. Some scientists think that *Diplodocus* lived like the present-day hippopotamus in rivers and lakes, where the water made its huge body buoyant and facilitated movement. Other scientists believe that the animal did not need the buoyancy of water to assist its movement. Its small, peg-like teeth were concentrated in the front of both jaws, forming a rake-like structure. They were unlikely to have been used for biting; they were most probably used for

raking food together and picking it up. *Diplodocus* fed on aquatic plants growing near the surface and ate them together with the organisms living in them (insect larvae, small crustaceans, water snails, etc.). *Diplodocus carnegii* is named after the industrialist A. Carnegie, who in 1909 financed excavations in Wyoming and Colorado (USA). These excavations resulted in the finding of six complete *Diplodocus* skeletons, which are now in the Pittsburgh museum. Casts of the skeletons are on view in many European museums.

B. M.: total length 25−27 m
G.A.: late Jurassic, 150 million years
G.D.: North America (Wyoming, Utah, Colorado)

Brachiosaurus brancai Janesch

A specifically African dinosaur, *Brachiosaurus brancai* was discovered by the German palaeontologists W. Janesch and E. Hen-
nig in Tendagur (East Africa) during a period from 1909 to 1910.
The assembled skeleton is on view in the Natural History Museum in Berlin. The posterior part of the *Brachiosaurus* body had
a shrunken appearance and differed in this respect from *Brontosaurus* and *Diplodocus*. This was because the fore limbs were
longer than the hind limbs. The humerus attained a length of 2.1
metres and is the longest humerus ever known. The small head
was perched on a long neck. The raised nostrils were situated on
top of the head and between them an arched bony ridge curved
back over the crown. The position of the nostrils and the long
fore limbs suggest that *Brachiosaurus* lived mainly in the water
and that, if danger threatened, it could submerge and still be able
to breathe through its slightly protruding nostrils. Its quite considerable height indicates that it might have frequented fairly
deep water. *Brachiosaurus* probably lived on aquatic plants and
grazed the vegetation growing at the bottom of lakes with its
strong teeth. Janesch believed that it lived on dry land, and
nibbled the twigs of cycads and conifers after the manner of
today's giraffes.

B.M.: total length 23 m
      height (including neck) 12 m
G.A.: late Jurassic, 150 million years
G.D.: east Africa

Monoclonius nasicornus Brown

This animal takes both its generic and its specific name from the single great horn seated on its nasal bone. The back of its skull was bordered by a bony collar which was actually an extension of the parietal bones. The collar protected the animal's most vulnerable spots—the back of its head and its neck. The body was compact and barrel-shaped and the legs were short and thick. The comparatively short tail evidently trailed on the ground as the animal walked. Like rhinoceroses, *Monoclonius* had a thick skin, which was broken up into a large number of irregular plates. Spatulate teeth were arranged in dense rows at the back of both jaws, the anterior margins of which were transformed into a beak- or pincer-like structure. *Monoclonius* was a typical terrestrial herbivore, chopping its food into small fragments rather than chewing it. It inhabited regions with small lakes, and dry raised ground with patches of trees and bushes.

B.M.: total length 5.4 m
       height of body 2.6 m
       length of skull, including collar, 1.42 m
G.A.: late Cretaceous, 80—70 million years
G.D.: North America (Montana and
       Alberta)

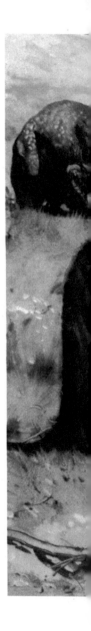

Triceratops prorsus Marsh

Triceratops is the last of the group of horned dinosaurs. It is named after the three horns (tri = three, ceras = horn) which adorned its imposing skull. Two horns grew from the forehead and the third—and smallest—was seated on the nasal bones. The back of the skull spread out to form a bony collar which protected the neck when the head was raised. The front of both jaws was converted to a kind of beak, enabling the animal to snip off the leaves and twigs of plants. The body resembled that of a rhinoceros and the thick skin was broken up into a large number of irregular polygonal plates. The limbs were thick and the hind legs were somewhat longer than the fore legs. The posture of the front feet was digitigrade, i.e. the weight was taken on the toes rather than on the whole foot. *Triceratops* inhabited regions

where swamps and lakes occurred together with higher, dry, flat ground dotted about with groves composed of sequoias, gingkos, poplars, oaks, maples and other trees. Here these animals roamed about singly or in small groups, just like rhinoceroses of today. Again like rhinoceroses, they probably used their horns for defence, or perhaps in combat with rivals in the mating season. The skull of an animal, which evidently fractured one of its horns while still quite young, is a very interesting find. The fracture healed and the animal lived to a good old age, as seen from the normal development of the second horn.

B.M.: total length 6 m
        height of body 2.6 m
        length of skull, including collar, 2 m
G.A.: late Cretaceous, 80 — 70 million years
G.D.: North America (Canada to Mexico)

Tyrannosaurus rex Osborn

Apart from numerous finds of isolated bones, *Tyrannosaurus* is known from two splendidly preserved skeletons found by B. Brown in northern Montana (USA). They are the attraction of the New York Natural History Museum, where they have been assembled as if they were fighting over prey. *Tyrannosaurus* was one of the largest predators which ever lived. Its flat-sided skull measured 1.4 metres and was armed with sharp, slightly recurved teeth fifteen to twenty centimetres long. Its small, puny fore limbs had three digits and at the most could only have been employed for holding prey. It was the powerful hind limbs that were used for locomotion. The tracks of *Tyrannosaurus* have also been preserved: the length of the steps—3.76 metres—shows that, even when walking slowly, it travelled at considerable speed. These predatory dinosaurs attacked the more cumbersome herbivorous ones, which were defenceless against their tremendous strength. With their huge teeth they tore off whole lumps of flesh from their victim's body and swallowed them. Some scientists are of the opinion that such great, heavy animals were not capable of sudden attack and suggest that they lived on carcasses. Whether it was a predator or a scavenger, traces of the teeth of *Tyrannosaurus* have definitely been found on the bones of many of its contemporaries.

B.M.: total length 10—14 m, height 5 m
G.A.: late Cretaceous, 80—70 million years
G.D.: North America (Montana, Wyoming)

Tarbosaurus bataar Maleev

Tarbosaurus was an Asian relative of some of the carnivorous American dinosaurs such as *Tyrannosaurus*. It belonged to a phylogenetically rather more conservative line than *Tyrannosaurus,* however, and was not so large. It had a relatively large skull and numerous long, sharp teeth in its jaws. Only its hind limbs were used for locomotion. Its stunted fore limbs, with their two digits, were probably employed simply for holding prey or for gripping the partner during copulation. These predacious creatures hunted herbivorous dinosaurs in the steppes and semi-steppes of what is now the Gobi desert, in inner Asia. At the end of the Mesozoic era, this region was not so inhospitable as it is today and did not dry up and become a desert until 50,000 years ago. In those days it possessed many lakes and rivers with a wealth of plants and animals. Complete *Tarbosaurus* skeletons have been recovered from this region by various palaeontological expeditions (American expeditions between 1922 and 1930, Soviet expeditions in 1946, 1948 and 1949, a Chinese—Soviet expedition in 1959—1960 and Polish—Mongolian expeditions between 1963 and 1965).

B.M.: total length 14 m
      height 6 m
G.A.: late Cretaceous, 70—65 million years
G.D.: inner Asia (Gobi desert)

Anatosaurus (= Trachodon) annectens Marsh

Anatosaurus was a curious dinosaur with a long, low skull and a wide, flat snout like a duck's bill. Its jaws were crowded with tiny teeth whose total number amounted to about 1,000. Its fore limbs were thinner than its hind limbs, but could still be used for locomotion. The webbing between the toes of its fore limbs shows that it was just as much at home in the water as on the land. Apart from skeletons, there in also a 'mummy', which is to be found in the New York Natural History Museum. It is obviously not the mummy itself, but a faithful replica imprinted in fine sandstone. *Anatosaurus* frequented lakes and rivers and was herbivorous.

B.M.: total length 9 m
G.A.: late Cretaceous, 80 – 70 million years
G.D.: North America (Montana, Wyoming)

Corythosaurus casuarius Brown   (following double-page) 44

This dinosaur was given its specific name after the helmet-like crest on its head, which resembled the 'helmet' of cassowaries. The nasal passages were open grooves leading to the top of the crest, the purpose of which may thus have been to enlarge the olfactory organs and improve their function. *Corythosaurus* had short fore limbs and the digits may possibly have been connected by webbing. The hind limbs were definitely not adapted for an aquatic life however. At present we cannot tell how far *Corythosaurus* was adapted to an aquatic mode of life. We know that these reptiles inhabited regions of the same type as the present-day Florida swamps and that they lived on aquatic plants. In the water they were safe from terrestrial predators, but they probably often fell prey to crocodiles.

B.M.: total length 9.5 m, height 4 m
G.A.: late Cretaceous, 80 – 70 million years
G.D.: North America (Canada)

Iguanodon bernissartensis Boulenger

Iguanodon became well-known through the discovery of twenty-nine more or less complete skeletons in Bernissart near Mons, Belgium, in 1878. Twenty-three assembled complete skeletons are on exhibition in the Institut Royal des Sciences Naturelles in Brussels. *Iguanodon* had an elongated, deep skull, with a laterally compressed snout. Its numerous flat, notched teeth were sometimes worn right down to the cylindrical roots, but were constantly replaced by new teeth formed in the gums. The body was covered with both small and large bony plates, forming a kind of armour. The fore limbs, which were much thinner and shorter than the hind limbs, were not used for locomotion, but may have been adapted for grasping food (the second and third digit each had a wide claw). The thumb was at right angles to the other digits and terminated in a horny 'dagger', probably used for defence. *Iguanodon* was herbivorous and lived on the shoots and twigs of trees and bushes. It liked damp lakeside regions, but does not appear to have turned to the water for safety, however, preferring to trust in the speed of its powerful hind limbs.

B.M.: total length 8 m
       height 5 m
G.A.: early Cretaceous, 120 million years
G.D.: western and central Europe

Compsognathus longipes Wagner

Compsognathus is ranked among the dinosaurs, but it could hardly be called a giant. It had a low, elongated skull, an extremely flexible neck and a relatively long tail. Its stunted fore limbs were useless for locomotion and were employed for grasping prey, but its hind limbs were relatively long and were adapted for running. It is interesting to note their marked resemblance to a bird's tarsus. The likeness is probably only a case of evolutionary convergence, however, although it has been claimed that these small dinosaurs could have been the ancestors of cursorial birds (ostriches, etc). *Compsognathus* inhabited the unforested, sandy shores of Mesozoic lagoons and lakes and evidently lived on whatever the water cast up on to the land. Scientists originally thought that it lived on insects and fruit, but the finding of the bones of a small lizard-like reptile in the abdominal cavity of a skeleton discovered near Solnhofen in Bavaria shows that *Compsognathus* was more than likely carnivorous. Tracks left by these reptiles in littoral sand and mud are also known. These tracks were described under the name *Ichnium lithographicum* and were initially thought to have been made by pterosaurs *(Rhamphorhynchus)* or primitive birds *(Archaeopteryx).*

B.M.: total length 60 cm
       length of skull 7.5 cm
G.A.: late Jurassic, 150 million years
G.D.: Europe (Bavaria)

Mystriosaurus bollensis Jaeger

Mystriosaurus was the first true crocodile. It had
a flat head with a very long, wide-tipped snout
equipped with many large teeth. Its back was
covered with armour, which began roughly above
the third cervical vertebra, extended over part of
the tail and was composed of rows of bony plates
whose edges fitted together. The marginal plates
of the armour had a longitudinal ridge which
grew increasingly thicker towards the tail and ran
down the centre of the caudal plates. During the
animal's lifetime, this ridge was covered, as in
present-day crocodiles, with horny outgrowths
which attained maximum size on the tail. The
limbs were adapted for swimming, although they
had not yet been converted to paddles and only
had webbing between the toes. *Mystriosaurus*
lived on fish and possibly on other marine vertebrates as well. Gastroliths—stones swallowed to
help in the processing of food—have been found
in these animals' abdominal cavities. They would
have collected these stones on the land, where
they evidently also laid their eggs, but their short,
puny fore limbs demonstrate that such visits were
rare and that their true environment was the sea.

B.M.: total length 4 m
G.A.: early Jurassic, 190—180 million years
G.D.: western Europe

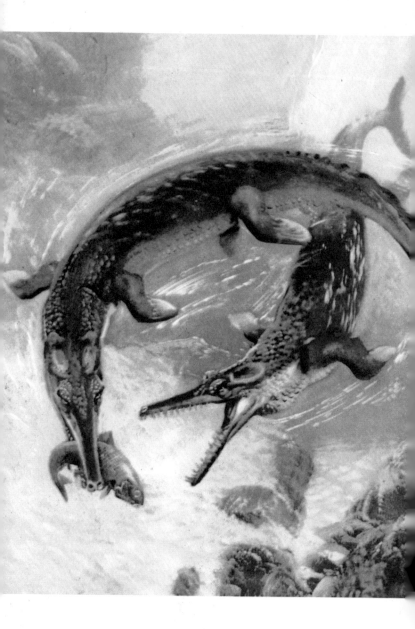

Metriorhynchus brachyrhynchus Deslongchamps

This animal was a crocodile, but was well adapted to a life in the open sea. Its tapering skull was moulded in front of the orbits in a characteristic scissors pattern (which could not, of course, be seen in the living animal). The nostrils, situated at the tip of the snout, allowed the animal to breathe with only a small portion of its head showing above the water. The teeth were markedly dimorphous (they existed in two distinct structural forms); on the premaxilla (a bone in the middle of the upper jaw) there were three pairs of exceptionally large teeth for grasping prey, while the rest of the teeth were smaller. *Metriorhynchus* did not possess the bony armour typical of the majority of crocodiles and was thus relatively light, an important factor for swimming. Its limbs were converted to paddles and the fore limbs, in particular, were short, wide and spatulate; the hind limbs were stronger and less modified. The powerful tail had a caudal fin, whose spiral movement was more important for propelling *Metriorhynchus* through the water than the reduced limbs. *Metriorhynchus* lived mainly on fish. We know nothing about its embryonic development, but it is unlikely to have laid eggs on the land because of its highly specialized limbs.

B.M.: total length 2.5 m
G.A.: late Jurassic, 150 million years
G.D.: western Europe

Mosasaurus mosasauroides Gaudry

Mosasaurus was a European cousin of the American *Tylosaurus* (see Pl. 50), with which it had many features in common. The first mosasaur skull was found in 1770 in lithographic limestone near Maastricht in Holland, and in 1795, for a bribe of 600 bottles of wine, was acquired for the Natural History Museum in Paris, where it was studied by G. Cuvier. The skull of mosasaurs tapered off into a short, conical process and their jaws were armed with massive, sharp, conical teeth. They had paddle-like limbs, with five digits on the fore limbs and four on the hind limbs. Their trunk terminated in a strong tail which, together with serpentine undulation of the whole body, contributed far more to the animal's locomotion than did the limbs. Mosasaurs (the name means 'sea-lizard') frequented the open sea and lived on fish, as we can see from their teeth. They remained near the surface and although they were able to dive, they evidently did not venture into very deep water.

B.M.: total length up to 12 m
G.A.: late Cretaceous, 70 million years
G.D.: western Europe

Tylosaurus dyspelor Cope

This great, scaly reptile, which was not unlike the present-day monitor lizards in appearance, had a triangular skull with a tapering, pointed snout. The lower jaw had secondary joints and could be folded like a pantograph, thereby enabling the animal to open its mouth extremely wide. The teeth were large, conical and sharp. The trunk was relatively short, but the tail was very long and had a fin-like border, especially along the dorsal ridge. The limbs were converted into paddles and the digits were encased in skin. The limbs were not the only organ of locomotion; *Tylosaurus* also moved with serpentine undulations of its whole body, especially the tail. These animals were predators and lived mainly on fish, although adult individuals probably preyed on marine reptiles, especially turtles, plesiosaurs and ichthyosaurs.

That such large prey put up a great struggle for its life is indicated by the presence, on the predator's bones, of traces of various injuries, mainly healed fractures of the jaws and ribs. Although food remains have been found in the body cavities of *Tylosaurus* specimens, no remains of embryos have ever been found. *Tylosaurus* does not seem to have been viviparous, but rather to have laid its eggs in shallow creeks, where the young stayed until they were able to venture out into the open sea.

B.M.: total length 8 m
G.A.: late Cretaceous, 80 million years
G.D.: North America (Kansas)

Plesiosaurus species

Plesiosaurus is the best-known genus of the European Mesozoic reptiles and over ninety species have been described (all from finds of incomplete skeletons), of which probably only three species are systematically valid. Plesiosaurs were marine animals with flipper-like limbs and like the ichthyosaurs they had an increased number of joints on the digits. The limbs were still rounded, however, and were not flattened and fin-like, as they were in ichthyosaurs. The neck was extremely long and flexible. This was most important because, judging from their limbs, plesiosaurs were not able to swim very fast and their serpentine neck was a great aid for catching the fish on which they lived. Plesiosaurs have been known to the public for a long time. The first skeleton to be found was described scientifically in 1824, but about 150 years previously (to be exact in 1678), the German physician and naturalist Anastasius Kirchner published a book entitled 'Mundus subterraneus' (The underground world), in which he depicted the skeletons of 'dragons' purported to have lived in ancient times in the region of Holzmaden. If we turn the picture of Kirchner's 'dragons' round, the wings become flippers and we find ourselves looking at plesiosaurs.

B.A.: total length 3—5 m
G.A.: early Jurassic, 170 million years
G.D.: western Europe (Germany, England)

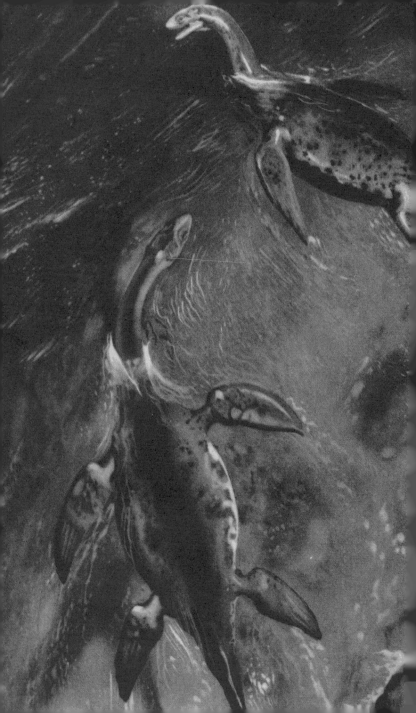

Cryptocleidus oxoniensis Phil.

This highly specialized plesiosaur was well adapted to life in the water, with its five-toed limbs forming effective paddles. *Cryptocleidus* inhabited the open sea and, like all plesiosaurs, it lived on fish; with its long, strong neck and its extremely flexible spine, it was no doubt expert at catching them. In the tree of evolution the genus *Cryptocleidus* appears to be an isolated branch of the plesiosaurs which became specialized very early on, did not survive the Jurassic period and evidently left no descendants. The area of its geographical distribution was very small and this further testifies to the marked phylogenetic isolation of this group of reptiles.

B.M.: total length 3.3 m
G. A.: late Jurassic, 150 million years
G.D.: western Europe (England)

Elasmosaurus platyurus Cope

Elasmosaurus is the largest known representative of the plesiosaurs, the reptiles with a snake-like neck. It had the longest neck length among the plesiosaurs, since a full seven metres of its total length of thirteen metres was accounted for by the neck. The relatively small head terminated in a short, 'bulldog' snout with sharp teeth which, especially in the front of the upper jaw, were very long and overlapped the lower jaw. The neck was composed of seventy-six vertebrae—a number not yet surpassed by any other animal, either living or extinct. It was extremely flexible and could be coiled in a snake-like manner. The limbs were of the paddle type. These plesiosaurs were predators inhabiting the open sea. Their highly flexible neck allowed them to swiftly seize their prey from some distance. They lived mainly on fish and cephalopods, but also ate certain reptiles (perhaps including pterosaurs).

B.M.: total length 13 m
G.A.: late Cretaceous, 80 million years
G.D.: North America (Kansas)

Stenopterygius quadridiscus Quenstedt

As well as complete skeletons, the impressions of the soft parts of the body of ichthyosaurs have also been preserved, in the form of dark borders round the skeleton. The ichthyosaur *Stenopterygius* was well adapted to an aquatic existence, its body having acquired a fish-like form. Its skull was extended into a kind of beak and was armed with a quantity of large teeth. The limbs had been transformed to fin-like structures. The tail terminated in a large, semicircular, leathery, vertical caudal fin and even a triangular dorsal fin was present. The habits of *Stenopterygius* were similar to those of present-day dolphins. It spent most of its life in the open sea, where it hunted fish, cephalopods and other animals. The abdominal cavity of skeletons of this ichthyosaur often contains the remains of such food. *Stenopterygius* was viviparous and the young were born by degrees, tail first. The skeletons of prenatal embryos are coiled in a specific manner. In some cases the skeletons of young individuals, sometimes incomplete, have been found in the abdominal cavity in an atypical position. These are not embryos, but appear to be the remains of food, showing that the newborn young were not safe even from members of their own kind.

B.M.: total length 2.5−3 m
G.A.: early Jurassic, 180−170 million years
G.D.: central and western Europe

Nannopterygius entheciodon Hulke

Nannopterygius is one of the later ichthyosaurs; its adaptation to a marine existence had progressed much further than that of geologically older species. Its head was attached closely to the body and there was practically no sign of a cervical spinal region. The fore and hind limbs were reduced to minimal proportions, while the tail was very long and exceptionally strong. It was the ichthyosaur's main locomotor organ, since the only function of the rudimentary limbs was to keep the body on an even keel. Like all ichthyosaurs, *Nannopterygius* evidently lived in the open sea. Its diet consisted of fish and various other marine animals (mainly cephalopods).

B.M.: total length unknown
G.A.: Jurassic, 150 million years
G.D.: western Europe (England)

Dimorphodon macronyx Buckland

Dimorphodon is the geologically oldest pterosaur (winged reptile) and is related to the rhamphorhynchids (see Pl. 57). It had an
abnormally large, bulky and rather terrifying-looking skull
whose weight was reduced by large cavities separated from each
other by thin bony partitions. Its structure, reminiscent of the
supporting arches of a bridge, prompted Richard Owen to de-
clare that, in so far as achieving great strength from light-weight
materials was concerned, no vertebrate was more economically
constructed. Otherwise, of course, the body structure of *Dimorphodon* displays many primitive characters, such as a very small
brain-pan. The jaws were toothed, with large, peg-like teeth in
the premaxilla and small teeth further back in the maxilla. It was
this dimorphodontism that gave the pterosaur its name. The neck
was strong and flexible and may have had a membranous pouch
on the under side. The fourth 'finger', which had long phalanges
and thick metacarpals, was used for stretching the flying membrane. We do not know whether *Dimorphodon* was able to fly
actively, i.e. flap its wings, or whether its flight was of the passive,
gliding type, but at all events it was a poorer flier than later
pterosaurs. Our knowledge of how *Dimorphodon* lived is also
very small. It probably inhabited coastal regions and had a very
varied diet.

B.M.: wing span 1.6 m
        length of skull 22 cm
G.A.: early Jurassic, 180—170 million years
G.D.: western Europe (England)

160

Rhamphorhynchus gemmingi v. Meyer

Rhamphorhynchus was a typical pterosaur, though by no means one of the largest. It had a sharp-pointed snout and widely spaced teeth like spikes, which protruded sideways from the mouth. They could certainly not have been used for biting, but only for gripping prey. Membranous wings were stretched between the fifth digits ('little fingers') and the body, and with these rhamphorhynchids could fly like bats. As distinct from bats' wings, however, the wings were narrow and pointed. The relatively long tail terminated in a rhomboid or pear-shaped flap of skin which acted as a rudder during flight (it was vertical and not, as previously supposed, horizontal). The short body was covered with fine hair—a most unusual feature in reptiles. Rhamphorhynchids inhabited sandy lakesides and caught their food (probably fish) by skimming over the water. They are known from complete skeletons, often with impressions of the soft parts of the body and the wings, found in Jurassic lake sediments in Bavaria and Würtemberg (Germany); the identity of remains found near Tendagur (East Africa) is more doubtful.

B.M.: total length, including tail, 40—50 cm
G.A.: late Jurassic, 150 million years
G.D.: western Europe

Pterodactylus antiquus Soemmering

Pterodactylus is another familiar pterosaur. Numerous complete skeletons are known from lithographic limestone near Solnhofen (Bavaria) and single bones and parts of skeletons have been found in western Europe. Remains of skin and tendons and impressions of the skin and wings have often been preserved on the Bavarian skeletons. The skin was wrinkled and scaleless. The body was short, the hind limbs relatively sturdy, the tail minute and the wings wide. These features tell us that the pterodactyl was a very poor flier and that it probably spent more time on the ground than in the air. Like a bat, it could evidently flap its wings and rest hanging upside down from the branch of a tree or a ledge of rock. It is also assumed that it could crawl along branches and climb trees like present-day fruit-bats. It must be stressed that any points of similarity between pterodactyls and bats are merely coincidental, however, and that the two are not in any way related. Pterodactyls probably lived in large flocks beside lakes and the sea and caught insects and small fish by flying over the surface of the water. We cannot say for certain whether they were diurnal or nocturnal animals.

B.M.: body length 10 — 15 cm
G.A.: late Jurassic, 150 million years
G.D.: western Europe

Pteranodon ingens Marsh

Pteranodon was the largest pterosaur of all time. Its remains are found comparatively frequently in Kansas (USA). The front of its skull was extended into a large, sharp-pointed, toothless 'beak' (the name means 'wings + no teeth'). The back of the skull was extended into a long, bony crest. According to some scientists, the latter was a kind of rudder, while others consider that its purpose was to counterbalance the long snout. The facial part of the skull and the brain-pan were very small. The neck was short, thick and very flexible; the body was greatly abbreviated. The first body vertebrae were fused to form a structure known as a notarium, to which the shoulder blade was attached by a joint. This was very important for the development of the flight muscles, because the thorax was very small. The fore limbs were

adapted for flying; the hind limbs were puny and would certainly not have been of any use on the ground, so that *Pteranodon* evidently spent most of its life in the air. Like the albatross today, it seems to have been able to make use of air currents and there are finds which suggest that it could fly as much as 100 kilometres out to sea. It lived mainly on fish and may also have eaten crustaceans. These pterosaurs laid their eggs on particular rocks, where they formed 'pteranodon islands'. The young were very small and the parents presumably fed them, like pelicans, from a pouch.

B.M.: wing span 8 m
G.A.: late Cretaceous, 80 million years
G.D.: North America (Kansas, Oregon)

'Proavis'

'Proavis' is a purely hypothetical form of primitive bird which is presumed by scientists to have existed, but has not yet been discovered. Certain similarities in skeletal structure show that we must look for the beginning of the avian phylogenetic line among the small reptiles of the the extinct Pseudosuchia group. We do not know to which species of this group the bird line can be traced back, or even when the reptile started to evolve into a bird, although we suppose that it happened some time during the transition from the Palaeozoic to the Mesozoic era, about 250 million years ago. We assume that *'Proavis'* had a snout with teeth and not a beak and that its fore limbs had not yet been transformed into wings. Along the sides of the limbs and on the tail, however, the scales had been converted to primitive feathers forming a simple apparatus which allowed the animal to glide, or more probably only to take long leaps, while running or when jumping from the branches of trees. It was thus not yet a bird in the proper meaning of the term, but just a climbing and jumping bird ancestor. Further evolution led to the formation of plumage, at first only on the wings, perhaps, and later on other parts of the body. Many new paleontological finds will have to be made before we know the whole story of avian evolution, however.

B.M.: not known
G.A.: not known (250 million years?)
G.D.: not known

Archaeopteryx lithographica v. Meyer

Archaeopteryx is the oldest known stage in the evolution of birds and is an interesting mixture of avian and reptilian characters. Its skull lacked a typical bird's beak and had a reptile's jaws with a row of tiny, blunt, conical teeth. The structure of the brain-pan was distinctly avian, however. The fore limbs had three free digits as in reptiles, but were covered with feathers with the same structure as those of birds. The hind limbs were typically avian, but the tail was long, as in reptiles. It is interesting to note the arrangement of the tail feathers, which formed a kind of palm-leaf pattern. *Archaeopteryx* was evidently a poor flier. Its long, unwieldy tail, its flat breastbone and the primitive structure of its fore limbs (wings) could only have permitted gliding, or at the most clumsy fluttering flight over short distances. It inhabited wooded regions in the vicinity of lakes. At one time it was thought that it lived on seeds and fruit of trees, which it obtained by climbing, using the free toes of its fore limbs. Recently the finding of a further specimen of *Archaeopteryx* upset these ideas, since the toes of the fore limbs showed the impressions of sharp, curved claws better suited for seizing prey than for climbing trees. In view of the tiny teeth, however, we cannot say what this prey was.

B.M.: total length 40 cm
G.A.: late Jurassic, 150 million years
G.D.: western Europe (Bavaria)

Ichthyornis victor Marsh

This Mesozoic bird, the size of a pigeon, had fully developed wings and a large ridge on its breastbone for insertion of the flight muscles. It did not possess a pygostyle, however, the caudal vertebrae being free. This raises the question of whether *Ichthyornis* had proper tail (steering) feathers, which are normally attached to the pygostyle. Despite this, *Ichthyornis* probably was a good flier and could safely undertake long journeys. It used to be stated that *Ichthyornis* had teeth, but the claim is still unsubstantiated. Jaws have unfortunately never been found together with a skull, and what was once thought to be an *Ichthyornis* jaw was found instead to belong to a young marine crocodilian reptile of the genus *Mosasaurus,* remains of which are common in the strata in which *Ichthyornis* remains are found. According to recent evidence, *Ichthyornis* lived in colonies on 'bird islands', from which it made expeditions far out to sea, where it caught fish swimming near the surface.

B.M.: height 20 cm
G.A.: late Cretaceous, 80 million years
G.D.: North America (Kansas and Texas)

Hesperornis regalis Marsh

The skeleton of this interesting bird was first discovered in 1870, by the American palaeontologist Professor O.C.Marsh, together with the bones of several marine reptiles. The skeleton of *Hesperornis* shows that it was an aquatic bird, and its structure displays signs of great specialization as well as numerous primitive characters. In general, *Hesperornis* resembled the present-day grebe. Like grebes, it had a long, narrow skull. The upper jaw had been converted to a beak, but still contained reptilian teeth, which were set in a groove (not in sockets). The tip of the beak (the premaxilla) was toothless. It is not clear how the lower jaw was constructed. A lower jaw ascribed to *Hesperornis* is suspiciously like a mosasaur jaw and since it was not directly connected to a skeleton, many scientists are sceptical about its identification. The breastbone of *Hesperornis* had no ridge and the wings had secondarily lost the power of flight and had been transformed to flippers, as in the case of penguins. The hind limbs resembled those of grebes or cormorants; of their three toes, connected by swimming membrane, the outer one was the longest and the inner one the shortest. Understandably, little is known about the plumage, but it may have been rather like that of an ostrich. *Hesperornis* was flightless and was also clumsy on the ground, but it was an expert swimmer and diver. It inhabited 'bird islands' near the coast and lived on fish.

B.M.: body length 1 m
G.A.: late Cretaceous, 80 million years
G.D.: North America (Kansas)

Triconodon mordax Owen

Triconodon was a very primitive mammal known only from finds of teeth and jaws. It had an elongated skull with a small, primitive brain-pan. It is not clear where it belongs in palaeontological classification. It was formerly included among the marsupials, but this is simply conjecture, because only its skull is known. We likewise know nothing of the embryonic development of triconodons. Although they existed only during the Jurassic period, triconodons were the dominant element of the mammalian fauna. In those days, mammals formed only a minor component of the animal population and lived almost literally in the shade of the dinosaurs. They constituted a world of their own, comprising small animals which lived either under the shelter of broadleaved plants or in the tops of trees and bushes. Although no larger than a domestic cat, in their own environment triconodons played the role of 'big cats' and hunted various smaller herbivorous or insectivorous mammals and small reptiles. It has even been suggested that they ate dinosaurs' eggs. Triconodons do not seem to have been of any great evolutionary importance; at any rate, among more recent mammalian faunas we do not know of any group which could be traced back to them.

B.M.: size of domestic cat
         length of lower jaw 4,5 cm
G.A.: late Jurassic, 170 – 150 million years
G.D.: western Europe

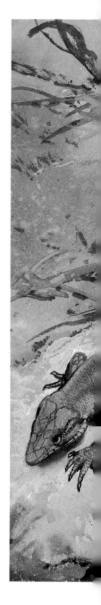

Andrias scheuchzeri Tschudi

Andrias scheuchzeri was a gigantic salamander whose bones were discovered long before it was known that it had extant relatives living in eastern Asia. It was found in Oeningen in Baden, Germany, in 1726, by Johann Jakub Scheuchzer, who believed that fossils were the remains of animals which died before Noah's Flood. Its round head and straight spine gave Scheuchzer the idea that the skeleton was a human one. He therefore described it as 'Homo diluvii testis' ('Man, a witness to the Flood'). It was not until 1811 that Cuvier recognized that Scheuchzer's 'godless sinner' was actually a giant salamander, which was then given the generic name *Andrias* (Greek for 'man image' or 'statue') and the specific name *scheuchzeri* after its discoverer. *Andrias scheuchzeri* inhabited the lower reaches of streams and small rivers. Skeletal remains found in Miocene lake deposits show that it was transported by water for only moderate distances. When young, it probably lived on aquatic worms and crustaceans and when adult on fish and frogs. The last living relatives of these interesting Cainozoic amphibians are to be found in China *(Andrias davidianus)* and Japan *(A. japonicus)*.

B.M.: body length 1 m and over
G.A.: late Miocene, 10 — 5 million years
G.D.: central Europe

Palaeobatrachus grandipes Giebel

Palaeobatrachus was a Tertiary frog resembling the present-day African clawed toad *(Xenopus)*. Its skeletal remains are plentiful in freshwater sediments in western Bohemia, in Geiseltal (German Democratic Republic) and in the German Federal Republic. They are sometimes preserved very well indeed, with impressions of the internal organs, muscles, nerves, blood vessels and epidermis, and with traces of colouring. Tadpoles and eggs have also been found. *Palaeobatrachus* had a relatively broad skull the shape of a Gothic arch. Its body was relatively large and the female was usually larger than the male (sexual dimorphism). These frogs lived permanently in water. Their bag-shaped lungs, on the dorsal side of their body, enabled them to remain submerged for long periods. They inhabited through-drainage basins or swamps where brown coal deposits were formed. Like the African clawed toad, they probably lived on small crustaceans, insect larvae and small fish and themselves provided sustenance for many other animals (crocodiles, snakes, aquatic birds, etc). The climatic change at the beginning of the Pliocene was a real catastrophe for *Palaeobatrachus,* which required warmth and, being specialized, was unable to adapt itself to the altered conditions.

B.M.: body length (without hind legs) 8 cm
G.A.: Miocene, 22–5 million years
G.D.: central Europe

Neocathartes species

This extinct genus of primitive vultures belongs to the New World vulture group, whose members are characterized by long legs, long toes, a longish body and a long, flat-sided beak with high nostrils. Their head and the lower part of their neck are devoid of feathers. Living species include the condor, the turkey vulture and the black vulture, to which *Neocathartes* bore the closest resemblance. *Neocathartes* was a rather squat vulture. It inhabited steppe country in what is now Wyoming (USA) and, like present-day vultures, it was probably a carrion-eater, although the black vulture, its nearest living relative, has a predilection for robbing the nests of aquatic birds.

B.M.: height 0.45 m
G.A.: Eocene, 40 million years
G.D.: North America (Wyoming)

Diatryma
steini Matthew et Granger

The American collector Stein found an almost complete skeleton of this bird and presented it to the Natural History Museum in New York. *Diatryma* was a comparatively large bird with a flat-sided head. The strong beak was not hooked at the tip and the lower mandible was massive, so that in some respects the whole beak was rather parrot-like. The neck was short and very thick and the body robust. The rudimentary wing bones show that *Diatryma* was flightless. The great, powerful legs were clearly adapted for running and had four toes, the third of which was the largest. The toes were armed with short, slightly curved, three-sided claws. These birds inhabited flat grassland with shrubs and trees or low hilly country. They lived singly or in pairs and no mass incidence of them is known. It is not altogether clear what their diet was, although some scientists are of the opinion that they lived very much as today's cassowaries do.

B.M.: height 2.15 m
      length of skull 0.45 m
G.A.: early Eocene, 55—50 million years
G.D.: North America (Wyoming)

Phororharcos inflatus Ameghino

This long-extinct, huge bird was a relative of today's seriemas (Cariamidae), which include the South American genus *Cariama*. It was much larger than the seriemas, however, and looked more like an ostrich in appearance. Its rudimentary wings and inability to fly seem to link *Phororharcos* with the ostriches, but, unlike ostriches, it had an enormous skull up to sixty centimetres long, armed with a powerful, hook-tipped beak. The structure of the beak and the large claws on the toes show that *Phororharcos* was a bird of prey. It raced over the grassy plateaus and hills of Patagonia, catching small reptiles and mammals. It was a specialized, local species of bird and took the place of large beasts of prey, of which in those days there were none in that part of the world.

B.M.: height 2—3 m
G.A.: Miocene, 20 million years
G.D.: South America (Patagonia)

Palaeolodus ambiguus Milne-Edwards

Palaeolodus was a Cainozoic flamingo and the precursor of present-day African species, but was rather smaller and more lightly built than its Recent relatives. A complete skeleton found in Saint Gérard-de-Puy in France is more like a stork's skeleton. The beak is not yet so typically curved as in flamingoes, but is conical and comparatively pointed. It seems that *Palaeolodus* was always to be found near water (mainly shallow pools and river shallows), where it hunted for food in the company of swans and various species of duck. Recent flamingoes strain mud through their typically curved beak, so that insect larvae and molluscs are left behind. To judge by the structure of its beak, *Palaeolodus* had a more diverse diet. It seems to have caught small vertebrates (fish and frogs), like present-day storks. Sexual dimorphism was demonstrated in *Palaeolodus,* as in many other birds. The females, similarly to those of other species, were originally described as a separate species, *Palaeolodus gracilipes.*

B.M.: shoulder height (without neck) 40 cm
G.A.: early Miocene, 22 — 19 million years
G.D.: western Europe

Aepyornis maximus Geoffroy

This gigantic bird was most closely related to the cassowaries, but lacked their typical crest. Its wing bones were reduced, but less so than in other related species. Its pectoral bone was thin and had no ridge and the flight muscles were undeveloped. *Aepyornis* resembled the New Zealand moa in body structure, but the likeness is merely a case of convergence, as the two groups evolved in different ways and from different ancestors. Large amounts of *Aepyornis* fossil material have been found, including whole skeletons now on show in various museums. Even eggs have actually been discovered, the largest one being thirty-five centimetres long and twenty-two centimetres wide, with a shell three millimetres thick. Both bones and eggs are found mainly in the southwestern and southern part of Madagascar. The eggs always lie in sand dunes and sun-heated sand seems to have played an important role in the hatching of the young. *Aepyornis* inhabited forest clearings and lived on larvae and berries, or on roots dug up from the ground. It did not die out until historical times and the beginning of its extinction coincides with the spread of agriculture. This forced it back from the forests into regions with swamps and lakes, where it was an easy prey for man or crocodiles.

B.M.: height 3 m
G.A.: Pleistocene to Recent,
      70,000 to 200 (?) years
G.D.: Madagascar

Dinornis maximus Owen

Until quite recent times, *Dinornis* still inhabited
New Zealand where the natives called it 'moa'. It
was a relative of the ostriches, but was taller and
larger in every respect. It had a strong skeleton,
powerful three-toed legs and completely reduced
wings. In relation to the body, the head was small,
with a pointed, short, flat and somewhat curved
beak. *Dinornis* inhabited regions covered with
forests and scrub and was a vegetarian. Man was
responsible for the disappearance of these birds.
It is reliably known that the Maoris still hunted
them at the beginning of the seventeenth century,
driving them into pits and robbing their nests.
The most important factor was farming, however,
for which the forests were cut and burnt down
and the ground was turned into arable land. The
moas seem to have died out at the end of the
seventeenth century, although there is actually
a nineteenth century report of hunters who
claimed to have caught sight of some of these
giant birds, but dared not venture to shoot them.

B.M.: height 3.6 m
G.A.: Pleistocene to Recent,
      40,000 — 200 (?) years
G.D.: New Zealand

Emeus crassus Owen

This ungainly moa had a sharp-pointed beak and a relatively long neck composed of twenty to twenty-one vertebrae. The bones of its fore limbs were either completely reduced, or had fused to form a single bone, with the result that the bird was flightless. It had short, thick legs with very short, strong tarsi. Soft parts of its body, such as tracheal rings (cartilage) or remnants of skin have been found, as well as single bones and whole skeletons. As they neared the head, the feathers grew shorter, until they finally turned into coarse hair; the head itself was probably bald. Numerous *Emeus* eggs have also been found, most of them broken, unfortunately. Eggs found in the abdominal cavity of a skeleton discovered in Pyramid Valley in New Zealand measured 179 by 134 millimetres. Another thing that makes this locality interesting is that *Emeus* skeletons are found there upright, sunk in the mud, but minus the head and the neck, which were probably carried away by water or by birds of prey. The Pyramid Valley finds suggest one of the causes of *Emeus* becoming extinct: the spread of agriculture forced it to retreat from the forest clearings and scrub to the less easily negotiable swamps, where instead of safety it found treacherous mud. It presumably died out in about the thirteenth or fourteenth century.

B.M.: height 1.5—1.8 m
G.A.: Pleistocene to Recent,
     70,000 to 600 years
G.D.: New Zealand (South Island)

Euryapteryx elephantopus Owen

This moa was probably the most robust of them all. It had a small head and a very wide, curved beak with a blunt, rounded tip. Its wings were completely reduced, so that it was flightless. On the other hand, it had strong legs with relatively strong tarsi. *Euryapteryx* mainly inhabited open country and was consequently known as the meadow moa, but it also ventured into the forests. Finds from caves suggest that it took shelter there from inclement weather, like the present-day kiwis. It also seems to have been a vegetarian, as indicated by the stones (gastroliths) found in the stomach cavity. Seeds (including conifer seeds), twigs from bushes and the remains of grasses have been found in the stomach cavity of a skeleton from the Pyramid Valley. Information that this great bird lived on molluscs, crustaceans and fish is based on Maori reports which are of doubtful authenticity, but cannot be unequivocally refuted. As distinct from other moas, *Euryapteryx* probably lived in flocks. It laid only two to four eggs at a time. The reason for this low fertility was possibly that *Euryapteryx* had no natural enemies except man.

B.M.: height 2.2 m
G.A.: Pleistocene to Recent
  70,000 – 800 years
G.D.: New Zealand (South Island)

Deltatheridium pretrituberculare Gregory et Sipmson

This very old mammal is known solely from finds in the Bayn-dzak and Nemegt areas in the Gobi Desert. So far only skulls and lower jaws have been discovered and practically nothing is known of the rest of its skeleton. The structure of the skull and jaws in part resembles that of insectivores allied to the shrews and tenrecs and in part that of carnivores or predacious marsupials. This raises the problem of where to classify *Deltatheridium* in the mammalian system. We cannot even definitely say whether it was a marsupial or a placental mammal. At present, it is assumed that it was a primitive insectivore closely related to the creodonts. The geological age of *Deltatheridium* is another hotly discussed question. The first finds were classified as late Cretaceous, i.e. at the end of the Mesozoic era, but some scientists held that *Deltatheridium* came from the overlying early Tertiary layers. That would have made a radical difference to the phylogenetic significance of this animal, as instead of a very old insectivore or primitive carnivore we should have had a representative of a phylogenetic line which, in the Tertiary era, when the evolution of other groups of mammals had already made considerable progress, remained at a very primitive level. A Polish-Mongolian expedition was fortunately able to confirm that *Deltatheridium* was a late Cretaceous form, however. We know very little about this animal's habits, but it is supposed that it caught small mammals, like today's predacious marsupials.

B.M.: length of skull 3.5 cm
G.A.: late Cretaceous, 80—70 million years
G.D.: Asia (Gobi Desert)

Andrewsarchus mongoliensis Osborn

This was the largest skull of all carnivores either living or extinct. Its skull alone, which was found by an American expedition in Mongolia and can be seen in the New York Natural History Museum, measured eighty-four centimetres, i.e. four times the length of a wolf's skull and double the length of the skull of the Alaska brown bear, which is regarded as the largest living carnivore. *Andrewsarchus* belongs to the creodonts ('flesh-tooth'), primitive carnivores derived from late Cretaceous insectivores. Like other members of this group, it had a relatively large skull, with

an extremely long, flat-sided snout. It had a full complement of teeth, with huge incisors. Of its four toes (on each foot), the first was already vestigial. The last joint of the toes terminated in a structure which was more like the hoof of a primitive ungulate than the claws of a carnivore. The habits of *Andrewsarchus* are still obscure; its anatomical structure, however, demonstrates that it was mainly a flesh-eater, but that it lived on a mixed diet, like Recent bears.

B.M.: body length 4 m
         shoulder height about 2 m
G.A.: late Eocene, 43—38 million years
G.D.: Asia (Mongolia)

Hyaenodon horridus Leidy

This animal belonged to a branch of the creodonts, which, after most of other members of the group died out at the end of the Eocene, persisted into the early Pliocene, probably because it was almost at the same level of development as the true carnivores and was thus able to go on competing with them for quite a long time. *Hyaenodon* was one of the larger creodonts. It had a long skull with a narrow snout—much longer in relation to the length of the skull than in canine carnivores, for instance. Its neck was shorter than its skull, while its body was long and robust and terminated in a long tail. It had five toes on both its fore and hind feet, the first of which was shorter than the rest. *Hyaenodon* resembled a Recent hyaena in appearance, but its much sharper teeth and well developed sectorials (carnassials) show that it had very different habits. *Hyaenodon* did not live on carrion, but hunted ungulates up to the size of a sheep.

B.M.: body length 1.4 m
      body height 0.6 m
      length of skull 27 cm
G.A.: early Oligocene, 37—32 million years
G.D.: North America

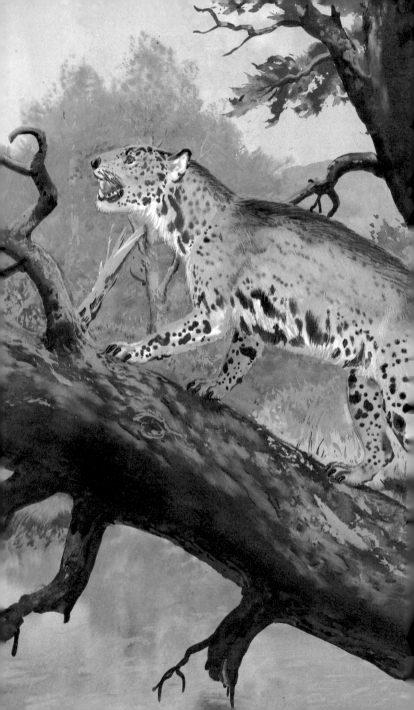

Oxyaena lupina Cope

Oxyaena belongs to the same group as *Hyaenodon*, although the two were very different. The diversity of form and adaptability of this group of creodonts enabled them to occupy a variety of ecological niches and thus to compete with the true carnivores for a long time. *Oxyaena* looked rather like a cat or a marten. It had a broad, low skull with a long facial part and a massive lower jaw, while its body and tail were long and its five-toed limbs were short. Unlike true carnivores, *Oxyaena* trod on the whole surface of its soles. Our knowledge of its habits is very small, but it is thought to have lived in a similar manner to the wolverine of today.

B.M.: body length 1 m
       length of skull 20 cm
G.A.: late Palaeocene to early Eocene,
       56—49 million years
G.D.: North America

Dinictis felina Leidy

Dinictis, as a very primitive type of feline carnivore, displayed evolutionary associations between the machairodontids (sabre-toothed cats) and feline carnivores. The shape of its skull is reminiscent of a felid skull rather than of the extremely short skull of machairodontids. Compared with those of the more recent machairods, its upper canines were comparatively small, but they nevertheless distinctly protruded from its mouth. Below the tips of the canines its lower jaw spread out in the form of a lobe. It had a longish body, a longer tail than machairods and slender, relatively short, five-toed limbs with only incompletely retractile claws. *Dinictis* looked like a small leopard and evidently its mode of life was similar to that of a leopard. It was probably not so particular about its food as its descendants, since reduction of the teeth was still in the early stages and *Dinictis* had not forgotten how to chew. Despite this, in its own environment it would have been a dreaded predator.

B.M.: body length 1.1 m
　　　 body height 0.6 m
G.A.: Oligocene, 35—25 million years
G.D.: North America (Dakota, Nebraska)

Pseudocynodictis gregarius Cope

This animal was a true canine carnivore. In the evolution of the canids it represents an early stage closely related to the miacids which lived at the beginning of the Tertiary. The finding of a complete skeleton made it possible to carry out a reconstruction of the whole animal. With its very long body and tail and its short, slender, five-toed limbs it brings to mind a civet-cat (viverrid), but at present it is not clear whether the two had the same ancestors or whether the likeness is merely a case of convergence. The brain-pan was constructed more on the lines of a miacid skull, but showed certain signs of evolutionary progress compared with miacids. Its teeth bore all the characters of true canid dentition and morphologically resembled the teeth of the Arctic fox. *Pseudocynodictis* evidently led a similar existence to Recent foxes or viverrids and hunted small vertebrates.

B.M.: body length 1.5 m
       body height 0.9 m
G.A.: early Oligocene, 35—32 million years
G.D.: North America

Phenacodus primaevus Cope

Phenacodus is one of the most well-known extinct mammals. It was described by Cope in 1873 from a complete skeleton, casts of which were sent to many museums. *Phenacodus* belongs to the extinct group Condylarthra, which played a very important role in the evolution of ungulates. There are certain features linking this group to primitive carnivores (creodonts) and insectivores and showing that they all had a common origin. *Phenacodus* had a small, elongated skull with a large occipital crest; it resembled the skull of creodonts rather than of ungulates. The structure of the incisors and molars increased the resemblance and even the limbs were more like those of a primitive carnivore than an ungulate, since they were short and sturdy. *Phenacodus* trod on the whole of its sole, after the manner of a bear. Its fore and hind limbs all had five digits, which spread out when the animal trod on them. The toes were tipped with nail-like claws. *Phenacodus* lived in groups in forests and wooded steppes and was omnivorous, like present-day pigs. Although not itself directly ancestral to the horses, *Phenacodus* gives us an idea of what that ancestral ungulate must have been like.

B.M.: body length 1.3—1.6 m
       shoulder height 0.55 m
G.A.: early Eocene, 55—49 million years
G.D.: North America (Wyoming, Wasatch)

Hyracotherium venticolum Cope

This ungulate, which is often described as 'Eohippus' meaning 'dawn horse', was the first stage in equine evolution, although it was still very far removed from the true horses. It had a low, elongated skull, a short neck and a vaulted back, so that its whole body appeared to be hunched up. In its jaws it had forty-four teeth, the largest number in any of the evolutionary stages of the horses. The molars were low and cusped as in tapirs, while the premolars were triangular (with three cusps) and very different in shape from the molars. The limbs were small and slight. The fore limb had five toes, but only four of them were used (the great toe no longer touched the ground). The hind limb likewise had five toes, but in this case only three of them were developed. Although the toes already had tiny hoofs, the animal still trod on the whole of them, causing them to splay out. *Hyracotherium* inhabited swampy forests like today's tapirs and lived mainly on leaves and young shoots. This explains its splayed toes, which kept it from sinking into the swampy ground. It walked along or took small jumps and sought refuge from enemies in the thickets. *Hyracotherium* produced several species, which spread over North America and even penetrated into Europe. In Europe they soon died out, but in America they gave rise to the evolutionary line of the true horses.

B.M.: body length 60 cm
G.A.: early Eocene, 55—49 million years
G.D.: North America

Mesohippus bairdii Leidy

Mesohippus, meaning 'intermediate horse', was the first link in the evolutionary line of the horses proper. Although no larger than a dog, it already looked like a miniature horse. Various parts of its body underwent marked evolutionary changes. The first premolar disappeared, the other premolars gradually acquired the appearance of molars, the crowns of both the premolars and the molars grew larger and the cusps joined together to form W-shaped walls. Dental cementum, which is normally present in more recent evolutionary stages of horses, was still absent in *Mesohippus.* The limbs were still comparatively short and both the fore and the hind limb had three spread toes. The middle toe was distinctly larger, however, and increasingly took the weight of the whole body; the animal now stood on a hoof and not on its toes. The metacarpal and metatarsal bones grew longer and the limb became adapted for running and trotting, thereby initiating the type of movement characteristic of Recent horses. *Mesohippus* inhabited grassy plains with trees and shrubs beside rivers and with groups of thornbushes on dry ground. It lived in large herds.

B.M.: shoulder height 60 cm
       length of body 115 cm
       length of skull 22 cm
G.A.: middle Oligocene, 32—26 million years
G.D.: North America (Nebraska)

Hyrachius eximius Leidy

Although it outwardly resembled a primitive horse, this animal was one of the earliest rhinoceroses. Some of its characteristics linked it to primitive tapirs. It was about the size of a sheep and had a low, flat skull (but no horns) and a slender body. Its limbs were relatively long, with four toes on the fore limbs and three on the hind ones, and were definitely better adapted for running than the legs of Recent rhinoceroses. *Hyrachius* inhabited open tropical forests and lived on the soft, fleshy plants growing at the margins of swamps and beside water. It shunned open country and it was left to its late Tertiary, and mainly to its Quaternary, descendants to venture further afield and take to the grasslands, where adaptation to the new conditions led to changes in their body structure, giving rise to the African and Asian rhinoceroses we know today.

B.M.: length 1.2 m
      height 0.75 m
G.A.: early and middle Eocene,
      55–45 million years
G.D.: North America (Wyoming)

Anthracotherium magnum Cuvier

Anthracotherium was a large, ungainly animal related to pigs and hippopotamuses. It had a huge skull with a long, narrow, flat-sided snout. Its dentition was characterized by extremely strong, spatulate incisors and hooked canines, which looked like the canines of carnivores rather than the fangs of a bear. There were five toes on the fore limbs (the first one was greatly reduced) and four on the hind limbs, where the outer digits were asymmetrically reduced (the second one more than the fifth). The outer digits of *Anthracotherium* were not reduced to the same degree as a pig's toes and the limbs were more like those of a hippopotamus. *Anthracotherium* inhabited forests and swamps in the basins of undrained lakes. It lived on aquatic plants and it is supposed that it plucked them with its strong, hooked canines. The spatulate incisors could have been used for digging in the mud. The hippopotamus is probably descended either directly from *Anthracotherium,* or from a related genus. *Anthracotherium* is so named because numerous skeletal remains have been found in soft (brown) coal ('anthrax' = coal, 'therium' = animal).

B.M.: length of trunk 1.8 m
      shoulder height 1.2 m
      length of skull 0.7 m
G.A.: early Oligocene, 35—32 million years
G.D.: western and central Europe

Merycoidodon culbertsoni Leidy

This exclusively North American ungulate is better known under the generic name *Oreodon*. Taxonomically, it belongs to an isolated group of even-toed ungulates (artiodactyls) related to camels. Its ancestors date back to the Eocene and its last descendants are known from the Pliocene, so that oreodonts, broadly speaking, lived throughout the whole of the Tertiary era. Their body was longish and the limbs short. Their fore limbs had five toes (although the first one was vestigial) and their hind limbs had four. The dentition resembles deer's teeth in structure, except for the strong canines which are very striking. Oreodonts lived in large herds and moved about from place to place. They seem to have had a predilection for well-watered regions, where food was plentiful and succulent. At one time, oreodonts were as plentiful in south Dakota as zebras are today in the steppes of North Africa.

B.M.: same size as sheep
        length of skull 20 cm
G.A.: early Oligocene (Oreodon beds),
        38—32 million years
G.D.: North America (Bad Lands, Dakota)

Hyracodon nebrascensis Leidy

Hyracodon's dentition resembled that of later rhinoceroses, but it was a much smaller animal and
differed very little in appearance from the primitive horses of which it was a contemporary. It
had a short, broad snout and lacked the typical
rhinoceros horn. Its long, slender limbs had three
digits — another respect in which it resembled
primitive horses. The Austrian palaeontologist O.
Abel was of the opinion that hyracodonts, during
subsequent evolution, would have developed
a one-toed limb like horses. Again like primitive
horses, hyracodonts inhabited open forests and
wooded steppes and turned from browsing foliage to grazing grass. They died out without leaving any descendants and they mark the end of the
phylogenetic branch of hornless, running rhinoceroses. Some scientists believe that the evolution of hyracodonts was imperilled in particular
by primitive horses, which developed parallel to
them and proved to be too strong competitors
for them.

B.M.: length of body 1.5 m
      height of body 0.75 m
G.A.: middle Oligocene,
      32—26 million years
G.D.: North America (Bad Lands, Dakota)

Metamynodon planifrons Scott et Osborn

Metamynodon, which is known from finds of whole skeletons, was a very primitive type of rhinoceros. In appearance it somewhat resembled a tapir, but was much larger. It had a thick-set body and short limbs and was hornless. Its fearsome-looking canines were more like those of a carnivore, but the rest of its teeth demonstrate that it was a vegetarian. It probably used its canines, like today's hippopotamuses, for pulling up the shoots of the aquatic plants on which it doubtless lived, as it inhabited marshy forests and wooded regions beside rivers.

B.M.: length of body 4.5 m
G.A.: early and middle Oligocene,
      35—30 million years
G.D.: North America, eastern Asia

Arsinoitherium zitteli Beadnell

Despite appearances, *Arsinoitherium* is not related to the rhinoceroses, but belongs to a completely extinct group, Embrithopoda. At present we know little of its origin and its kinship to other groups of mammals is equally obscure, although it seems to stand closest to proboscideans and hyraxes. *Arsinoitherium* was a large ungulate whose four-toed, column-like limbs were very primitively built. They show that *Arsinoitherium* was a slow-moving animal which inhabited marshy country like Recent hippopotamuses or Mesozoic dinosaurs. The nasal bones were surmounted by a pair of huge, sharp, bony horns, fused together at the base, while two much smaller horns grew from the frontal bones. Despite their menacing appearance, these creatures were vegetarians and lived on plants which they found in damp forests and at the margin of swamps. They seem to have been a specific African species with limited geographic distribution. Their exotic generic name comes from the name of the Egyptian princess Arsinoe, a daughter of Pharaoh Ptolemy I (third century B.C.), after whom an ancient religious centre in the Fayum oasis was also once named.

B.M.: body length 3 m
G.A.: early Oligocene,
          37 — 32 million years
G.D.: North Africa (Fayum)

Uintatherium mirabile Marsh

Uintatherium was the size of an African rhinoceros and had a similarly armed head, but it belonged to the extinct group Dinocerata, which was more closely related to the elephants. It is interesting to note that gigantic forms had already evolved in this group of primitive ungulates during the early Tertiary, when the groups of ungulates living today were still very small. *Uintatherium* had a flat, concave skull — a feature not found in any other animal. Its cranial cavity was unwontedly small, but the walls of the brain-pan were exceedingly thick. The weight of the skull was lessened by air cells in the wall of the brainpan, like those in an elephant's skull. The skull was surmounted by three pairs of 'horns'; these were actually bony outgrowths covered, during the animal's lifetime, with skin. The most striking teeth were the sabre-like canines, which resembled the canines of sabre-toothed cats (machairods) and were larger and stronger in the males than in the females. *Uintatherium* lived near water and used its sabre-like canines to pluck the aquatic and marsh plants which comprised its diet. These animals died out without leaving any descendants.

B.M.: body length 3.3 m
       length of skull 0.75 m
G.A.: middle Eocene, 45—40 million years
G.D.: North America (Utah, Wyoming)

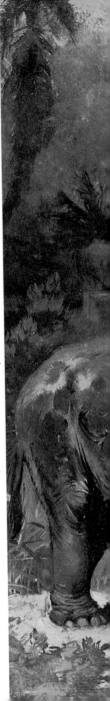

Brontotherium platyceras Osborn

This animal was a member of the extinct group of the Brontotheriidae or Titanotheridae, distant relatives of horses, tapirs and rhinoceroses. Alongside horses and elephants, brontotheres were the most important order of their time. Despite the huge size of its most recent representatives, this group remained at a primitive stage of development. Brontotheres were large, ungainly animals with a small, low skull, in which the tiny eyes were set well to the front. The brain was surprisingly small, so that the animal's intelligence was very low. Horny outgrowths sprouted from the nasal bones; unlike the horns of rhinoceroses they were composed of bone and in the living animal were covered with

skin, like the horns of Recent giraffes. Herds of brontotheres roamed the shrub-strewn grasslands of North America, where there were plenty of pools with succulent aquatic plants. They died out comparatively suddenly at the end of the early Oligocene and their disappearance was associated with climatic changes (a drier climate) which increased the extent of the dry steppes. It is interesting to note that the Sioux Indians (Dakota) were already acquainted with brontothere bones. They imagined them to be the bones of 'thunder horses' which leaped down from the sky during storms and whose hooves were responsible for the sound of thunder.

B.M.: body length 4.3 m, body height 2.5 m
G.A.: early Oligocene, 38—32 million years
G.D.: North America

Indricotherium parvum Chow

Indricotherium was the largest dry-land mammal known to have existed. Although nobody would think so to look at it, it takes its place in the zoological system among the rhinoceroses. It had a long, low, hornless skull and vaulted frontal and nasal bones. Its front teeth were reduced to a single pair of incisors in either jaw, but they were conical and so large that they looked like small tusks. The upper incisors pointed straight downwards, while the lower ones jutted outwards. The upper lip was evidently extremely mobile. The neck was very long, the trunk robust and the limbs long and thick, column-like. *Indricotherium* inhabited dry grasslands with a few trees, where it congregated in small herds. Its type of dentition, its mobile upper lip and its long legs and neck indicate that it lived on the leaves and twigs of tall trees, which it cropped like present-day giraffes. We could thus claim that it was a kind of 'giraffe-like rhinoceros'.

B.M.: body length 8 m
        shoulder height 5.5 m
G.A.: early Oligocene, 37 – 32 million years
G.D.: inner Asia (Mongolia, China)

Moeritherium lyonsi Andrews

Moeritherium, or 'dawn elephant', was discovered by American expeditions which went to Africa in 1901 to 1905 and in 1907. Although a proboscidean, it was more like a tapir in appearance; instead of a trunk it had an extremely mobile upper lip. The structure of its jaws was also reminiscent of a tapir's. It had a complete set of teeth (in more recent proboscideans at least some teeth are reduced), which were simple and cusped. Both sets of second incisors (upper and lower) were enlarged and converted to short, peg-like tusks. This is one of the features which ranks *Moeritherium* among the proboscideans. The body was robust and the limbs long and thick. *Moeritherium* is thought to have inhabited thickets beside water and marshes in steppe country, and to have led a similar life to the present-day hippopotamus. Several related species have been found in the classic Egyptian locality in Fayum, north of lake Moeris (hence their generic name), but so far none have been found anywhere else. *Moeritherium* was formerly regarded as the direct ancestor of the proboscideans. However its isolated incidence has led modern scientists to conclude that it is not the ancestral form, but an aberrant, atypical species very close to the original (and still unknown) ancestor.

B.M.: shoulder height 0.7 m
G.A.: late Eocene, 45—40 million years
G.D.: North Africa (Fayum)

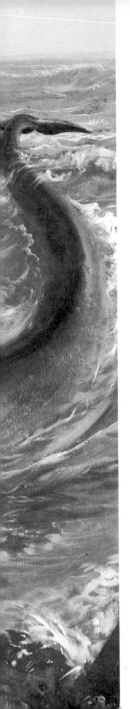

Basilosaurus
(= Zeuglodon) cetoides Owen

Basilosaurus is the most curious cetacean we know. Its skeleton, discovered in 1832, was reconstructed as that of a 'sea serpent'. In 1834 the American palaeontologist Harlan named it *Basilosaurus,* i.e. 'king of the saurians', mistakenly supposing that it was the skeleton of a reptile. In 1839, the English palaeontologist Richard Owen recognized it for the skeleton of a cetacean and changed its generic name to *Zeuglodon* (the rules of priority give precedence to the first, inaccurate name, however). Many *Basilosaurus* skeletons have been found and some of them have had interesting histories. In 1845, Albert Koch, a German naturalist, put together a skeleton from bones discovered in Alabama in North America and travelled all over Europe, exhibiting it for money. *Basilosaurus* had a relatively slim body, with a short neck and extremely long trunk and tail. The special construction of its vertebrae made its body very flexible. The fore limbs were more or less normally developed, while the hind limbs were reduced. The saw-edged teeth were useful for catching fish. It is supposed that *Basilosaurus* was less well adapted for submerging than today's cetaceans.

B.M.: body length up to 20 m
       length of skull 1.5 m
G.A.: late Eocene, 43—38 million years
G.D.: North America (Alabama)

Thylacosmilus atrox Riggs

This highly specialized carnivorous marsupial had a tapering
snout with particularly long upper jaws (maxillaria). The long,
curved upper canines were similarly developed to those of machairods (sabre-toothed cats), but *Thylacosmilus* was not related
to these animals and the likeness was simply a case of convergence produced by a similar mode of life. *Thylacosmilus* had
long, sabre-like upper canines and short, blunt, peg-like lower
canines. The incisors were missing altogether and the other teeth
were severely reduced, but, as distinct from machairods, their
number was complete. In the region of the symphysis (midline),
the lower jaw widened to form lobes providing 'pouches' or
'sheaths' for the sabre-like fangs. The cervical vertebrae were

very strong and to some extent resembled the vertebrae of machairods. At present we do not know what the legs looked like. *Thylacosmilus* led a similar type of life to machairods. It belonged to the specific Tertiary fauna of South America and when more highly developed mammals began to infiltrate South America from the north, it was unable to hold its ground in competition with placental carnivores.

B.M.: body length 1.3 m
       length of skull 0.22 m
G.A.: Pliocene (Araucarian), 5—3 million years
G.D.: South America (Argentina)

Machairodus cultridens Roth et Wagner

Machairodus was the largest carnivore of its day. It was formerly described as 'sabre-toothed tiger', but in fact, machairods have nothing in common with tigers; they belonged to a separate branch of felids (Machairodontidae), which became specialized at an early stage of their evolution. The most striking feature of

machairodontids were their long, curved upper canines, which, in the most highly developed forms, protruded from their mouth. The lower canines were mostly reduced. The beginnings of this branch can be traced back to the Miocene, while extreme forms of machairodontids are known from the Pliocene and the beginning of the Pleistocene. As their canines grew to enormous lengths, their other teeth were progressively reduced, to a far greater extent than in the true felids. *Machairodus cultridens* inhabited grasslands, where it hunted ungulates (hipparions, antelopes, giraffes and pigs). It did not bite its prey to death like true cats do, but with the aid of its powerful neck muscles it plunged its fangs into its victim's body and slit the throat or the belly with a single jerk of its head. Its reduced dentition shows that it consumed only the viscera and the blood. Consequently, when the ungulate population diminished at the beginning of the Pleistocene, the number of machairods also started to decrease. Relatively small species of machairodontids survived for quite a long time, but in the end they too died out.

B.M.: same size as tiger
G.A.: early Pliocene,
        5—4,5 million years
G.D.: southern and western Europe

Dicrocerus elegans Lartet

This small deer was a relative of the muntjac and according to some scientists they both had the same ancestors. It was the first member of the cervids to possess antlers. The antlers were still quite primitive and had no tines; they were worn only by the males. The antlers of early species had no rose at their base and were thus probably not shed; typical cervid roses are found only in more recent forms. These species shed the antlers together with part of the pedicle, so that the older the animal, the shorter and wider the pedicle. *Dicrocerus* resembled *Palaeomeryx* in appearance, but in addition to possessing antlers it had more intricately constructed molars. It probably came from Asia, from the region where the true deer originated and evolved. It inhabited forests in the temperate belt and in Europe it was typical of the Miocene. It died out at the beginning of the Pliocene without leaving any descendants.

B.M.: same size as roe deer
G.A.: late Miocene, 10—5 million years
G.D.: central Europe (related species in Asia)

Palaeomeryx kaupi v. Meyer

Palaeomeryx was one of the oldest of the cervids.
It was related to the muntjacs and probably also
to the primitive giraffes. Neither the male nor the
female *Palaeomeryx* had antlers, but the male
had large, curved canines, which protruded from
its jaws. The teeth of these animals were characterized by a 'palaeomeryx fold'—a small crease in
the enamel on the inner (lingual) aspect of the
molars, between the anterior and posterior wall
of the crown. This feature does not occur in more
recent cervids. *Palaeomeryx* inhabited Tertiary
forests, especially of a damp and marshy type.
This can be seen from its hooves, which spread
out fanwise, to prevent its legs from sinking into
the soft, muddy soil. *Palaeomeryx* was a characteristic animal of the early part of the late Tertiary. It died out at the close of the Miocene.

B.M.: size of small roe deer
G.A.: middle Miocene, 14—11 million years
G.D.: Europe

Merychippus primus Osborn

Merychippus inhabited the grasslands of North America, where it lived on tough steppe grasses. Its teeth were well adapted for dealing with this hard food. The molars had high crowns to allow for rapid attrition and the cementum formed on the crown not only coated the outer wall of the tooth, but also filled the spaces between the cusps. The premolars were almost identical in form to the molars; they were separated from the canines by a space. It is interesting to note that both sexes had canines (in true horses they are developed only in the stallions). The limbs were adapted for running on a hard surface. They were slim and had three toes, although the lateral toes had ceased to function and had shifted so high up the foot that they no longer touched the ground. The ulna and the radius were fused as in true horses and so were the tibia and the fibula. *Merychippus* lived in herds, like present-day zebras. Phylogenetically, it was a very important step in the evolution of horses, because from it came direct evolutionary lines leading to the three-toed hipparions on the one hand and to the one-toed horses, asses and zebras on the other.

B.M.: shoulder height 1 m
G.A.: middle Miocene, 14 — 10 million years
G.D.: North America (Nebraska)

Hipparion mediterraneum Hensel

This animal was descended from the North American hipparions, which spread from North America to Asia and from there to Europe. In the early Pliocene, hipparions formed huge herds which gave the Eurasian fauna its typical character. Hipparions had three toes, but placed their weight on the middle one only; the other two toes were rudimentary and were so high up on the foot that they never touched the ground. Instead of the original four- to five-toed supporting pad, a rebound mechanism which allowed greater speed of movement, mainly in trotting, developed (the foot could be picked up better). Loading of the middle digit was also associated with a change in the connective tissue apparatus and hence with a change in the proportions of the limbs, in particular attenuation and lengthening of the distal part, a typical feature of runners. The long molars had a complex structure, and were adapted for crushing the leaves and stems of steppe plants and grasses. Hipparions inhabited the broad grasslands of southern Europe and followed the same mode of life as present-day zebras in the African steppes. They were the culminating point of the main phylogenetic branch of the equids (horses are only a side branch!) and died out at the transition from the Tertiary to the Quaternary, without achieving monodactyly, the development of only a single digit.

B.M.: same size as zebra
G.A.: early Pliocene, 5—4.5 million years
G.D.: Europe

Alticamelus latus Matthew

Alticamelus was a rather grotesque but highly specialized animal. Although akin to camels, it looked very much like a giraffe. Its head was relatively small compared with the rest of its body, its neck was long, as a result of lengthening of the cervical vertebrae (especially the first and the third), and its legs were long and stilt-like, with the elbow and knee joints on the same level. *Alticamelus* walked on its toes only. They were transformed to cushioned plates like those of Recent camels. Its strange body structure gives us plenty of information on its mode of life and habits. *Alticamelus* obviously inhabited dry grasslands with groups of trees. It moved about singly or in small groups, like today's giraffes, and like them browsed upon the high foliage. Since in this respect it had no competitors, it survived a relatively long time. As a highly specialized genus it died out without leaving any descendants, however.

B.M.: height 3.5 m
G.A.: middle and late Miocene (and early Pliocene?),
       14—5 million years
G.D.: North America (Colorado)

Palaeotapirus helveticus v. Meyer

Palaeotapirus resembled the tapirs of today so closely that some scientists refuse to count it as a separate genus and include it in the Recent genus *Tapirus*. The differences are indeed very slight. Compared with early Tertiary tapirs the premolars of *Palaeotapirus* are very much like the molars in shape, a feature typical of more recent tapirs. *Palaeotapirus* was not different from Recent tapirs in appearance, except, perhaps, for its colouring, about which we unfortunately know nothing, however. Like Recent tapirs, it was adapted to a life in marshy forests with a moderately warm climate. Only a few fossil remains have been preserved in swampy regions, however—decidedly fewer than

would correspond to the actual size of the *Palaeotapirus* population. That is because humic acids formed in decaying vegetation in the marshy soil decomposed the greater part of their bones, so that practically all that is left of these animals is their teeth. *Palaeotapirus* survived in the temperate belt up to the beginning of the Pleistocene, but the climatic changes which took place at the beginning of this period caused it to retreat into the tropics and it found its last sanctuary in the Malayan Peninsula region and South America.

B.M.: shoulder height about 1 m
G.A.: Oligocene, 32—26 million years
G.D.: western and central Europe

Teleoceras fossiger Cope

The name of this very unusual rhinoceros can be freely translated as 'very long rhinoceros'. *Teleoceras* had a long, rhinoceros-type head and its pointed nasal bones were surmounted, in the males, by a small, thick horn. Its barrel-shaped body was a little longer, perhaps, than is usually the case in rhinoceroses of today, while its limbs were shorter—so short, in fact, that its belly almost touched the ground. The evidence indicates that *Teleoceras* lived in water, like the present-day hippopotamus; hence its short limbs, which, like those of a hippopotamus, were used for swimming rather than for walking. Despite its area of distribution (North America), *Teleoceras* does not seem to have been of American origin, but rather to have been the descendant of Asian rhinoceroses which migrated to North America in the early Tertiary. *Teleoceras* is known only in North America, however, and Egyptian and Libyan finds once described under this name are now known to belong to other genera.

B.M.: body length 4 m
       body height 1 m
G.A.: early Miocene to early Pliocene,
      20—3 million years
G.D.: North America

253

Gomphotherium angustidens Cuvier

This animal, also known under the generic names *Triphodon* and *Bunolophodon,* was a relatively primitive proboscidean of the mastodon group. It had a rather long skull with a bulging forehead and high nostrils, indicating that it had a short trunk. The tusks, of which there was a pair in either jaw, were comparatively short. The upper tusks were longer than the lower; they curved downwards and their outer surface was covered with enamel, while the lower tusks were not. There were six teeth in the upper jaw and five in the lower jaw. The teeth were cusped and the pairs of cusps (outer and inner) joined to form ridges. The lower jaw was long and shovel-like and supported the short tapir-like trunk, which did not hang down. The body was relatively short and the legs long and thick. A complete *Gomphotherium* skeleton, from Sansan in France, is assembled in the natural history museum in Paris. *Gomphotherium* inhabited dry wooded regions near lakes, while a specialized form, *Gomphotherium angustidens subtapiroides,* lived in swamps, like tapirs.

B.M.: at highest point of back 2.3—2.5 m
G.A.: late Miocene, 11—6 million years
G.D.: western and central Europe

Tetralophodon angustidens Kaup

Tetralophodon angustidens was descended directly from *Gomphotherium,* and like *Gomphotherium* it was characterized by a long, high skull, but it had short jaws. The upper tusks, which were longer than the lower, were almost straight and pointed slightly outwards and downwards; they were circular in cross section and had no enamel. The lower tusks were much smaller and shorter and were oval in cross section. The complete absence of lower tusks in some animals is regarded as sexual dimorphism (were these the females?). *Tetralophodon* had larger teeth than its forebears and there was a greater number of ridges on their crowns. In subsequent evolution, this increase in the number of ridges led to lamellization of the teeth as we know it in true elephants. *Tetralophodon* also had a longer trunk than its forebears (though not so long as the trunk of true elephants). It hung down between its tusks, over the shortened lower jaw. *Tetralophodon* inhabited forests and evidently lived on foliage and twigs. It was the direct ancestor of *Anancus arvernensis,* which represents the last phase in the evolution of the European mastodons.

B.M.: height 2—2.7 m
G.A.: early Pliocene, 5—4 million years
G.D.: Europe

Platybelodon grangeri Osborn

This highly specialized mastodon had a very long skull, a wide, flat premaxilla and small, short upper tusks pointing sharply downwards. The lower jaw started off by being narrow, but then suddenly widened to a shovel-like structure into which two huge, flat incisors were set. The anterior edge of these incisors was sharp and bevelled like a chisel; their microscopic structure is indicative of unusual hardness and strength. The animal did not possess a proper trunk, but it had a muscular upper lip, which did not stretch beyond its lower tusks and may have been used, together with its tongue, for raking in the food from its spatulate lower jaw. *Platybelodon* frequented lakesides and river banks and lived on aquatic plants, or perhaps on their roots, which it dug out of the mud with its lower jaw. The geographical distribution of these animals is very interesting, since all the known finds have come from the Tung gur table-land on the southeastern margin of the Gobi Desert. The reader may be surprised to learn of proboscideans occurring at such high altitudes. With increasing specialization of the mastodons, however, it is normal to observe their retreat from the lowland forests to the mountains and in South America some mastodons lived high up in the Andes.

B.M.: shoulder height 1.65 m
         length of skull, with lower jaw, 1.75 m
G.A.: late Miocene, 11—6 million years
G.D.: inner Asia (Mongolia)

Deinotherium giganteum Kaup

This species, which belongs to an independent, extinct branch of proboscideans with no descendants, was not very different from true elephants in appearance, although it had a somewhat shorter trunk and its column-like legs were longer in proportion to its body than those of elephants. Its most characteristic feature was its lower jaw, which turned down almost at right angles and bore a pair of strong, relatively short, recurved tusks; it possessed no upper tusks. The molars were reminiscent of tapir or mastodon teeth and show that deinotheres became an independent evolutionary branch very early on. Isolated deinothere bones, teeth and tusks have been known to science for a very long time, but because of their structure they were thought to be the remains of tapirs, hippopotamuses or other aquatic mammals. The finding of a whole deinothere skull in Eppelsheim (German Federal Republic) in 1832 allowed the German naturalists Kaup and Klippstein to rank it definitively among the proboscideans, however. Their classification was splendidly vindicated by finds of two whole skeletons in Bohemia in 1853 and 1883. Deinotheres inhabited damp forests, where they probably lived on foliage and soft tree shoots. This conclusion is based on the shape of their teeth, their curiously formed lower tusks, their short trunk, their long limbs and, indirectly, on their steady tendency to increasing height.

B.M.: height 3 m
G.A.: Pliocene, 4—2 million years
G.D.: Europe (related species in N. Africa)

Anancus
arvernensis Croizet et Jobert

This proboscidean survived from the Pliocene (the last of the Tertiary periods) into
the early Pleistocene. It was like a true elephant in appearance, but had shorter legs
and a wide, elongated skull, armed with
long, straight tusks (its generic name
Anancus, means 'without a curve'). The
tusks were defence weapons. The molars
were not composed of lamellae like those
of true elephants, but had cusps, like tapir
and pig molars; they were useful for chopping off leaves and succulent plants, but
not for cropping grass. This means that
Anancus lived on foliage, and finds of its
bones among other fossils is always a sign
of the presence of deciduous forests. At the
transition from the Pliocene to the Pleistocene this mastodon was still abundant, but
in the early Pleistocene, as the forests receded before the steadily expanding grasslands, its numbers diminished until it finally
disappeared altogether at the end of the
early Pleistocene. In Recent animal associations it was replaced by the true elephants.

B.M.: height 2.5 m
G.A.: late Pliocene and early Pleistocene,
        3—1.5 million years
G.D.: Europe (west, centre and south-east)

Archidiscodon meridionalis Nesti

The great southern elephant took the stage among the European
mammalian fauna as the symbol of a new epoch, the beginning
of the Quaternary era and the Pleistocene period. It was a direct
descendant of *Archidiscodon planifrons,* the oldest known true
elephant, which probably came from Asia or North Africa. The
earliest European immigrants (finds in Chagny, France, for instance) had unmistakable links with this species, although they
were morphologically already a separate species. The great
southern elephant resembled the Indian elephant in appearance;
its back was straight or slightly arched and did not slope down
from the shoulders like the African elephant's. It had a shorter

skull than *A. planifrons*. The huge tusks of the males first of all projected obliquely outwards and then curved S-wise inwards. The females' tusks were thinner and less elevated and curved inwards in a lyre-like pattern. Because of this the females were originally described as a separate species, *Elephas lyrodon*. The great southern elephant was not a particularly specialized species. It inhabited savanna, bush-steppe and woodland, but seems not to have frequented true steppe country. It occurred mainly in western and southern Europe.

B.M.: shoulder height 3.5—3.8 m
G.A.: early Pleistocene, 1,700,000—550,000 years
G.D.: Europe (west and south)

Palaeoloxodon antiquus Falconer

The straight-tusked elephant, a typical elephant of the warm periods of the European Pleistocene, is generally thought to have evolved in the earliest part of the Pleistocene from the great southern elephant, as a branch adapted to a warm climate, although according to other views it is of Asian origin. *Palaeoloxodon* was larger than the woolly mammoth. Its head was small in relation to its body and it had huge, straight tusks, with slightly curved tips, and long legs. Many isolated bones and teeth of this elephant have been found, but comparatively few complete skeletons. *Palaeoloxodon* inhabited forests and grasslands dotted about with deciduous trees, while some finds show that it even penetrated as far as the conifer forests of the temperate belt. It was a typical animal of the European interglacials, starting with the Cromerian. As the climate grew colder, it retreated from central to southern Europe and was replaced by either the steppe mammoth or the woolly mammoth. In the Eem interglacial it was hunted by primitive man, to whose activities we owe many finds of its bones (mainly in central European travertines). When the Eem interglacial ended the straight-tusked elephant withdrew to the Mediterranean region and its last representatives died out in Spain, in the last phase of the Würm glacial.

B.M.: height about 4 m
G.A.: middle and late Pleistocene,
     550,000 – 70,000 years
G.D.: Europe (except north)

Palaeoloxodon falconeri Busk

This animal, regarded as a pygmy form of elephant, evolved as a result of isolation on the islands of the Mediterranean (Malta, Cyprus, Crete, Sicily and Sardinia). The development of pygmy forms under such conditions is by no means unusual. Pygmy deer, hippopotamuses and other mammals inhabited these islands together with pygmy elephants. Unfavourable climatic conditions, as well as geographical isolation, seem to have played a role in the evolution of pygmy forms. The straight-tusked elephant *(Palaeoloxodon antiquus)* is considered to be the initial form of these pygmy elephants, but it is at present not clear whether the insular forms should be regarded as separate species, or only as local races. Pygmy elephants lived in the Mediterranean region in the last glacial periods. Individual bones and large skeletal units are found relatively often. It is presumed that it was some such find in a cave in Sicily or Malta which gave rise to the legend of Polyphemus, the one-eyed giant who was fought by the Greek hero Odysseus. The nasal opening in the middle of the skull was presumably wrongly taken to be an eye socket.

B.M.: shoulder height 0.9 m
G.A.: late Pleistocene,
         200,000 — 10,000 years
G.D.: Europe (Mediterranean region)

Mammuthus trogontherii Pohlig

The steppe mammoth is named (in Latin) after the beaver-like mammal *Trogontherium,* because their bones were found together. In earlier systematics it was classified, with a number of North American elephants, in a separate genus, *Parelephas,* but recent systematics rank it among the mammoths. It was the first stage in the evolution of the steppe and tundra elephants and an ancestor of the woolly mammoth of later glacial periods. Its skull was shorter than that of the great southern elephant. The males had spiral tusks with a recurved tip, while the females had thinner and only slightly curved tusks. The tusks grew to considerable lengths and the largest one known must have measured about five metres on the living animal. The mammoth was the first elephant to become adapted to life in the steppe, to a tough grass diet and even, in time, during the Mindel glacial, to cold steppes. It behaved increasingly like a cold-loving species and retreated northwards when the climate grew warmer. At the end of the Mindel glacial, the steppe mammoth was superseded by the woolly mammoth and by the beginning of the Riss glacial it had become extinct.

B.M.: shoulder height 4 — 4.5 m
G.A.: middle Pleistocene,
        600,000 — 370,000 years
G.D.: central Europe

Mammuthus
primigenius fraasi Dietrich

This interesting proboscidean of the middle Pleistocene of central Europe is still a subject of frequent discussion. Some experts are of the opinion that it is a specific, very primitive subspecies of *Mammuthus primigenius,* while others consider that it is more akin to the steppe mammoth *(M. trogontherii).* In all likelihood it is a local, ancient form from Steinheim gravels (Steinheim a.d. Murr, German Federal Republic), because it has so far not been reliably demonstrated anywhere else. A complete skeleton from Steinheim can be seen in the Natural Science Cabinet in Stuttgart. Fraas's mammoth was one of the largest European elephants and had long, column-like, five-toed limbs. It lived on grass and frequented open country inhabited by both warm- and cold-loving species. It seems to have occurred over a very short period only (the Holstein interglacial) and in the Riss glacial it was superseded by typical mammoth forms such as the woolly mammoth.

B.M.: height 4.3 m
G.A.: middle Pleistocene
       (Holstein interglacial),
       370,000 — 300,000 years
G.D.: central Europe (Germany)

Mammuthus primigenius Blumenbach

The woolly mammoth is without question the best known animal of the Pleistocene. The mammoth was adapted to life in cold steppe country; its adaptation was manifested in diminution of the size of the ears (which were no longer needed as fans) and in the growth of hair and of a fat hump. The woolly mammoth was often hunted by palaeolithic hunters, who also painted it on the walls of caves, engraved its likeness in bone and ivory and made statuettes of it. These artistic creations, like the mammoth 'mummies' found in the permafrost of Siberia, give us exact information on what these animals looked like. At the end of the last glacial period, the mammals followed the shrinking ice sheets northwards and north-eastwards and the last of them died out in Siberia at the beginning of the postglacial. Palaeolithic hunters had nothing to do with the extinction of the mammoth; when the cold steppes disappeared at the end of the last glacial period, the mammoths vanished too, since they were unable to adapt themselves to a different environment.

B.M.: European mammoth: height 3—3.5 m
      Siberian mammoth: height 2.75
      total length 5.4 m
G.A.: middle and late Pleistocene,
      300,000—10,000 years
G.D.: Europe, north Asia, North America

Mammuthus columbi Falconer

Like the emperor mammoth, the Columbian mammoth was also a descendant of mammoths which immigrated to North America during the Irvingtonian time (which roughly approximates to the Holstein interglacial in Europe). It inhabited the south-eastern part of the USA (South Carolina, Georgia, Louisiana) and may have extended still further south into Mexico. It was a large elephant, with curiously twisted tusks. The Amherst Museum (USA) possesses a whole skeleton found near Melbourne in Florida. The Columbian mammoth inhabited warm steppes with meandering rivers, or the regions round river deltas, where it lived in the company of horses, bisons, camels *(Camelops)*, steppe antelopes *(Capromeryx)*, armadilloes *(Glyptodon)* and edentates *(Northotherium)*. It died out at the end of the Pleistocene.

B.M.: shoulder height 3.7 m
G.A.: late Pleistocene, 70,000–40,000 years
G.D.: North America (south-east of USA)

Mammuthus imperator Leidy

The emperor mammoth lived in the southern part of the Great Plains of North America. It was descended from the great southern elephant *(Archidiscodon meridionalis)*, which immigrated to North America during either the Aftonian interglacial (corresponding to the Cromerian interglacial in Europe) or the Irvingtonian time. The emperor mammoth colonized the western and central part of the USA, from California, via Texas, Oklahoma and Kansas, to Nebraska, Wyoming and Montana in the north. Splendidly preserved skeletons have been found in the asphalt lake of Rancho la Brea in Los Angeles (California). The emperor mammoth was larger than even the largest African elephant. It had a high skull and its tusks first of all diverged and then curved upwards and backwards in a great arc. The tusks were huge and one found in Texas measured 4.2 metres. The emperor mammoth was a steppe-dweller, as seen from the concomitant fauna—steppe antelopes *(Capromeryx, Odocoileus)*, camels *(Tanupolama)* and edentates *(Mylodon)*. It vanished during the late Pleistocene.

B.M.: height 4 m
G.A.: late Pleistocene, 70,000 — 40,000 years
G.D.: North America (western and middle USA)

Mastodon americanus Kerr

Bones of this the commonest American mastodon are found quite frequently, so that it is one of the most familiar exhibits in American museums. It was a typical zygolophodontous type of mastodon, whose molars were characterized by deep depressions between the ridge-like walls. It had a long and relatively low skull. Its upper tusks were large, curved and circular in section, while its lower tusks were much thinner and not more than twenty centimetres long. The females had no lower tusks and their upper tusks were only slightly curved and were shorter and thinner than those of the males. As distinct from European mastodons, which died out in the early Pleistocene at the latest, *Mastodon americanus* was still living at the end of the Pleistocene, when the Wisconsin ice sheet receded. It was a contemporary of the mammoth and like it had a long, dark brown, hairy coat. It was this which enabled it to survive the cold winters of the Wisconsin glacial and venture as far north as Alaska, for example. *Mastodon americanus* was also a contemporary of man, who evidently hunted it. In the state of New York, its bones were found near the remains of an encampment fire, and near Pineville (Missouri) a primitive engraving, probably representing this mastodon, was found on a deer's bone.

B.M.: shoulder height 3 m
G.A.: middle and late Pleistocene,
 300,000 — 10,000(?) years
G.D.: North America to Alaska

Dicerorhinus etruscus Falconer

This relatively small, long-legged rhinoceros was typical of the early European Pleistocene. Isolated bones have been found in a whole number of places, but the only complete skeletons known came from Sénèze (France) and, more recently, Voigtstedt (German Democratic Republic—two skeletons). The second of these last two finds, which is the skeleton of a young animal changing its deciduous for its permanent teeth, is one of the most valuable early Pleistocene discoveries. The Etruscan rhinoceros is generally considered to have been a foliage-eater, but its menu was not particularly limited and it evidently frequented forest and savanna and bush-steppe. It had a special predilection for wooded river valleys. In the middle Pleistocene the Etruscan rhinoceros was succeeded by Merck's rhinoceros *(Dicerorhinus kirchbergensis)* which inhabited the same environment.

B.M.: total length 2.5 m
        shoulder height 1.5 m
G.A.: late Pliocene to middle Pleistocene,
        2,9 million—450,000 years
G.D.: Europe (in western Europe further north
        than in eastern Europe)

Dicerorhinus kirchbergensis Jäger

This species is generally known as Merck's rhinoceros. Jäger described it under the name *kirchbergensis,* which he later altered to *mercki* in honour of Counsellor Merck, a friend of the German poet Goethe. The rules of nomenclature insist that the first description applies, however, and not even the author himself can change it. The name 'Merck's rhinoceros' nevertheless stuck as the popular designation of this species. Merck's rhinoceros was a typical animal of the more recent interglacials. There is some confusion over its origin. Some scientists regard it as a descendant of the Etruscan rhinoceros, while others see it only as its ecological successor (a species living under the same conditions)

and regard identical characters as mere convergence (outer resemblance without phylogenetic association). Unfortunately, we so far do not possess a complete skeleton of Merck's rhinoceros, so that this and many other questions are still unresolved. Merck's rhinoceros inhabited deciduous wood, parkland and treeless grassland. It was hunted by early Palaeolithic man, as seen from numerous finds of its bones in Palaeolithic encampments in the last interglacial, in Ehringsdorf, German Democratic Republic, for example. It died out in central Europe at the end of the Eem interglacial and only in Spain survived into the first part of the Würm glacial.

B.M.: bigger than the Two-horned African Rhinoceros
G.A.: late Pleistocene, 370,000 — 70,000 years
G.D.: central and southern Europe as far as Caucasus

Coelodonta antiquitatis Blumenbach

The woolly rhinoceros is known as the faithful companion of the mammoth. Although a typical animal of the more recent glacials, it was not of European origin. We must look for its ancestors among the early Pleistocene rhinoceroses of Nihowan (China), which migrated north and north-east across Siberia and probably had already achieved considerable adaptation to a cold climate in Siberia. Like the mammoth, the woolly rhinoceros was clad in reddish brown hair, which on the back of its head and neck formed a longish mane. Information on the appearance of the woolly rhinoceros is provided by numerous cave drawings and by finds of 'mummies' near Starunia (Poland) and in Siberia. The woolly rhinoceros lived on grass and its main area of distribution was the cold steppes of recent glacials. It died out in Europe at the end of the last glacial, but it may have migrated in the wake of the receding ice-sheet to the north and north-east and it is thus possible that small herds of woolly rhinoceroses persisted in Siberia a little longer than in Europe.

B.M.: total length 3.5 m
          shoulder height 1.6 m
G.A.: late Pleistocene,
          400,000—25,000 years
G.D.: Europe, northern Asia (Siberia)

Elasmotherium sibiricum Fischer

The giant 'unicorn' was probably the largest true rhinoceros that ever lived. Its skull, which was almost one metre long, bore a single conical horn measuring one and a half to two metres. The horn was not seated on the nasal bones, as in the majority of rhinoceroses, but higher up, on the edge of the frontal bones. Individual bones that have been found tell us that *Elasmotherium* had a robust and rather unwieldy body with three-toed limbs. It was evidently descended from late Tertiary rhinoceroses of south-eastern Asia. Descendants of these rhinoceroses had already penetrated into eastern Europe in the early Pleistocene and eventually settled there. *Elasmotherium* was at home in the vast, flat steppes of what is now the south of Russia and never spread into western Europe, which in those days was covered with forests. *Elasmotherium* marks the culmination of a special branch of rhinoceroses adapted to life in unwooded steppes. Its teeth were even better suited than a horse's for crushing dry steppe grass. As the highest evolutionary form of its kind, it had no close relatives and died out during the Riss glacial without leaving any descendants.

B.M.: larger than white rhinoceros
G.A.: middle Pleistocene,
        230,000 — 200,000 years
G.D.: south-eastern Europe

Homotherium species

'Sabre-toothed tigers' or 'scimitar cats' (the few species of the genus *Homotherium*), which survived from the Tertiary era into the early Quaternary, were the largest carnivores of their day. They were characterized by exceptionally large upper canines, which in the true cats attained a much smaller size during phylogenesis. The canines were made even sharper by a saw-like ridge on the inner aspect of their crown. Sabre-toothed tigers inhabited steppes and hunted large ungulates. We can conclude from the structure of their teeth that they lived only on the blood and entrails of their prey, so that every sabre-toothed tiger had to catch several animals daily before its hunger was satisfied. When deterioration of the climatic conditions in the middle Pleistocene caused the vast steppes to disappear and decimated the herds of ungulates, the number of sabre-toothed tigers also diminished. It is not altogether certain just when the last of them died out. Up to now it was supposed that they did not survive the Mindel (Elster) glacial, but a number of recent findings indicate that their extinction came much later.

B.M.: size of tiger or panther
G.A.: late Pliocene to middle Pleistocene,
        3 million to 400,000(?) years
G.D.: Europe, southern Asia

Panthera spelaea Goldfuss

The cave lion, the largest and best known feline carnivore of the European glacials, was larger than an African lion. Cave paintings show that the males did not possess a mane and that their tail was not 'tasselled'. Cave lions had a long, thick coat, however, like the winter coat of Siberian tigers. They inhabited cold steppes and, in interglacials, bush-steppes and wooded regions. Horses were their main prey and cave paintings always show cave lions in the company of horses (cf. the dependence of Recent African lions on zebras). Unlike African lions, which live in groups or prides, cave lions lived solitarily. Their bones and skeletons are always found isolated and there are no known cave paintings in which they appear in a group. They were named 'cave' lions after finds of their bones in caves. In Europe they died out at the end of the last glacial period. It has not been reliably demonstrated that the Holocene lions of the Balkan Peninsula and Asia Minor are actually their descendants.

B.M.: total length 2 m
        shoulder height 1.2 m
G.A.: late Pleistocene,
        370,000 − 10,000(?) years
G.D.: Europe

294

Ursus spelaeus Rosenmüller

Like the mammoth and the woolly rhinoceros, the cave bear is one of the most typical animals of the Pleistocene. Its name is fully warranted, as its bones have been found in large numbers in many European caves. Cave bears of all ages frequented caves. They spent the winter there, gave birth to their young there and died there when they were old. Consequently, in the course of time, whole layers of bones, almost entirely those of cave bears, were formed in many caves. The cave bear was about a third larger than the brown bear and was more terrifying in appearance. It was nevertheless largely a vegetarian and in the summer, particularly, it lived entirely on a plant diet. The evidence is to be found in its flat molars, which are often very severely worn down. The cave bear was hunted intensively by early Palaeolithic hunters, but it was not they who endangered its existence. Cave bears were affected much more adversely by reduction of the forests in the last glacial period. The cold, grassy steppe did not provide them with sufficient sustenance and they died out during the first half of the last (Würm) glacial.

B.M.: same size as grizzly bear
G.A.: late Pleistocene, 270,000 — 20,000 years
G.D.: Europe (without most northerly parts),
       south-western Asia (Caucasus)

Megaloceros giganteus Blumenbach

The giant deer or Irish elk was neither a deer nor an elk, but formed an independent, specific group, related to fallow deer. It is known from finds of more or less whole skeletons in Irish peat-bogs. Giant deer were plentiful in the early and late Pleistocene, but were never so numerous as other species of mammals. A typical forest form of *Megaloceros* had already evolved during the middle Pleistocene, perhaps from ancestors which migrated to Europe from Asia. During their further evolution in Europe, the giant deer increased in size in general and their antlers in particular. The largest measurable set of antlers so far known has a span of 3.7 metres. Such antlers obviously made a permanent existence in the forest impossible and so the gigant deer moved to the cold steppes and the tundra. They held their head and neck horizontally like reindeer; they did not form herds, but lived solitarily like elks. At the end of the last glacial period they gradually died out and only in western Europe (Ireland) persisted a little longer.

B.M.: size of elk
G.A.: late Pleistocene,
          350,000 — 12,000 years
          in central and western Europe
          350,000 — 40,000 years
          in eastern Europe
G.D.: Europe, inner Asia

Capra ibex Linné

Although certain bones from early Pleistocene strata have been claimed to be those of ibexes, the first substantiated evidence of the history of these animals comes from the Riss (penultimate) glacial. It comprises fragments of a skull with slightly diverging horns, which was found in the sand and gravel of the river Saale near Camburg (German Federal Republic). The find was described as *Capra (Ibex) camburgensis* Toepfer and is regarded as the initial form of early Pleistocene ibexes. Ibexes inhabited upland and partly wooded steppes. In the glacial periods they were obliged to descend from their plateaus to the river valleys and lowlands and in the warmer interglacials they returned to the mountains. This gave rise to disunited populations, with a number of isolated local forms, in the various mountain systems (the Pyrenees, Alps, Carpathians, etc.) and to a tangle of names of subspecies, races and forms, confusing even to an expert. During the early Pleistocene, ibexes colonized all the young mountain ranges of southern and central Europe and penetrated via Transsylvania into the Crimea and Palestine. They were often the favoured game of Palaeolithic hunters, as can be seen from the cultist manner in which these stored their trophies. Today, ibexes are to be found in the Pyrenees and Alps and in the Caucasus, the mountains of north-eastern Africa, Asia Minor, the Middle East and inner Asia.

B.M.: shoulder height about 1 m
G.A.: late Pleistocene to Recent,
      200,000 — 0 years
G.D.: central and southern Europe, inner Asia

Rangifer tarandus Linné

The reindeer was a highly typical animal of the cold steppes and tundras of the more recent glacial periods, but there are many obscurities associated with it. It appeared in Europe at the end of the Günz glacial and in all subsequent glacials. There are abundant finds from the Würm period, but pre-Würm finds are meagre and consist mainly of fragments of antlers. The phylogenetic origin of the reindeer is likewise obscure. The structure of its antlers is reminiscent of certain early Pleistocene European deer, but the likeness seems to be only superficial. The reindeer evidently arrived in Europe already adapted to Arctic conditions. This is borne out by the fact that it disappeared from the European fauna during warmer periods. We cannot say when, where or how the reindeer acquired this adaptation to a cold climate. Many subspecies and races are differentiated among Recent reindeer, the main distinguishing features being the colour of the coat and the pattern of the antlers. The marked variability of reindeers' antlers and the fragmentary nature of the finds makes it almost impossible to apply these systems to the identification of fossil reindeer. After a great deal of discussion it is now accepted that European Pleistocene reindeer belonged to the north European species *Rangifer tarandus.* Since it was still plentiful at the end of the Würm glacial, when many other species had died out, the reindeer was the main game of Magdalenian hunters ('reindeer hunters'). Expansion of the temperate belt forests at the beginning of the Holocene forced the reindeer to retreat further north and today the scanty remains of this once widespread species are to be found only in Scandinavia.

B.M.: shoulder height 1.2 m
        body length 1.1 m
G.A.: middle Pleistocene to Recent, 600,000 − 0 years
G.D.: Europe

Canis familiaris Linné

The dog is the first animal to have been intentionally domesticated. It was already very important in prehistoric human societies as food, for guarding dwellings and later herds, and also as a hunting companion. The beginnings of domestication seem to go back to the days of late Palaeolithic hunters, before the end of the Pleistocene. The widespread utilization and distribution of the dog was the outcome of the development of farming (the Neolithic agricultural revolution), when the dog came to be used as a multi-purpose watch-dog. It is not known who the dog's ancestors were, but the rapid spread of dogs during the Neolithic age shows that they must have been common animals—probably wolves, whose area of distribution included Europe, Asia and North and Central America. The smaller southern forms in particular could have been readily domesticated (the Iraqi wolf *Canis lupus pallipes* comes into consideration, for example). The kinship of the dog with wolves is demonstrated by both their morphological and their physiological similarity (dogs can be crossed with wolves) and numerous experiments have shown that young wolves are easily tamed. During thousands of years of domestication, the dog has lost much of the wolf's characteristic behaviour. Changes in build and in the length and colouring of the coat, etc, are the result of intentional selection. Several races of dog were already known in the Neolithic age. Fashion has been responsible for the appearance and disappearance of many breeds of dog and it is interesting to note that the majority of races and breeds in existence today are not more than one hundred years old.

B.M.: varied
G.A.: late Pleistocene to Recent, 16,000(?)—0 years
G.D.: general

GEOLOGICAL ERAS AND PERIODS

Dating of periods from The Geological Time Table compiled by F. W. B. Van Eysinga 3rd edition 1975.

	Era	Period	Millions of years ago
	Quaternary	Holocene or Recent	0.01
		Pleistocene	1.8
The Phanerozoic, the age of manifest life	Cainozoic	Pliocene	5
		Miocene	22
		Oligocene	38
	Tertiary	Eocene	55
		Palaeocene	65
	Mesozoic	Cretaceous	140
		Jurassic	195
		Triassic	230
	Palaeozoic	Permian	280
		Carboniferous*	345
		Devonian	395
		Silurian	435
		Ordovician	500
		Cambrian	570
The Cryptozoic, the age of concealed life	Proterozoic		2,600
	Precambrian		
	Archaeozoic		3,500
	Origin of Earth		c. 4,500

* Instead of the Carboniferous, American stratigraphy distinguishes two separate periods—Mississippian and Pennsylvanian.

BIBLIOGRAPHY

COLBERT H.: Evolution of the Vertebrates. — Wiley & Sons, New York, 1966

HUENE F. v.: Palaeontologie und Phylogenie der niederen Tetrapoden. — Fischer, Jena, 1956

KAHLKE H. D.: Ausgrabungen auf vier Kontinenten. — Urania, Leipzig—Jena—Berlin, 1967

KAHLKE H. D.: Ausgrabungen in aller Welt. — Urania, Leipzig—Jena—Berlin, 1972

KURTEN B.: Pleistocene Mammals of Europe — Weidenfeld & Nicolson, London, 1968

LAVOCAT, R.: Histoire des Mammifères. — Seuil, Paris, 1967

LAVOCAT R. et al.: Faunes et Flores préhistoriques de l'Europe occidentale. — Boubée et Cie, Paris, 1966

MORE H. C. et al.: Treatise on Invertebrate Paleontology. — University Kansas Press, Kansas, 1953

MÜLLER A. H.: Lehrbuch der Paläozoologie I—III. — Fischer, Jena, 1953—1970

PIVETEAU J. et al.: Traité de Paléontologie I—VII. — Masson, Paris, 1952—1962

ROMER A. S.: Vertebrate Palaentology. — The University of Chicago Press, Chicago—London, 1971

RUDWICK M. J. S.: The Meaning of Fossils. — Macdonald, London—American Elsevier. Inc., New York, 1972

STIRTON A.: Time, Life and Man. — Wiley & Sons, New York, 1959

THENIUS E.: Versteinerte Urkunden. — Springer, Berlin—Göttingen—Heidelberg, 1963

THENIUS E.: Grundzüge der Verbreitungsgeschichte der Säugetiere. — Fischer, Jena, 1972

THENIUS E. & HOFER H.: Stammgeschichte der Säugetiere. — Springer, Berlin—Göttingen—Heidelberg, 1960

INDEX

Acanthodians 70
Aegiromena aquila 58
Aepyornis maximus 188
Alticamelus latus 248
Anancus arvernensis 262
Anatosaurus annectens 132
*Andrewsarchus
    mongoliensis* 198
Andrias scheuchzeri 176
*Anthracotherium
    magnum* 216
*Archaeopteryx
    lithographica* 168
Archelon ischyros 112
*Archidiscodon
    meridionalis* 264
Aristocystites bohemicus 58
Arsinoitherium zitteli 224

Basilosaurus cetoides 234
Bothriolepis canadensis 68
Brachiosaurus brancai 122
Brontosaurus excelsus 118
*Brontotherium
    platyceras* 228
Brooksella 52

Canis familiaris 302
Capra ibex 298
Charnia 48
*Chelyderpeton
    germanicus* 84

Chonophylum grandis 65
Climatius 70
Coelodonta antiquitatis 286
Compsognathus longipes 138
Conocoryphe sulzeri 56
Corals 60
*Corythosaurus
casuarius* 132
Cryptocleidus oxoniensis 150

Deinotherium giganteum 260
*Deltatheridium
pretrituberculare* 196
Diadectes phaseolinus 86
Diatryma steini 182
Dicrocerus elegans 240
Dicerorhinus etruscus 282
*Dicerorhinus
kirchbergensis* 284
Dickinsonia 48
Dimetrodon incisivus 90
*Dimorphodon
macronyx* 158
Dinictis felina 204
Dinornis maximus 190
Diplodocus carnegii 120
*Diplovertebron
punctatum* 80
*Discosauriscus
pulcherrimus* 82
*Drepanaspis
gemuendensis* 66

*Edaphosaurus
pogonias* 88, 90
Elasmosaurus platyurus 152
*Elasmotherium
sibiricum* 288
Ellipsocephalus hoffi 54
Emeus crassus 192
Entelophyllum prosperum 60
*Euryapteryx
elephantopus* 194
Eusthenopteron foordi 76

*Favosites
tachlowitzensis* 60, 65

*Gomphotherium
angustidens* 254

Henodus chelyops 100
Hesperornis regalis 172
Heterostraci 66
*Hipparion
mediterraneum* 246
Homotherium sp. 290
Hyaenodon horridus 200
Hyrachius eximius 214
Hyracodon nebrascensis 220
*Hyracotherium
venticolum* 210

Ichthyornis victor 170
Ichthyostega sp. 78

Iguanodon bernissartensis 136
Indricotherium parvum 230

Letoverpeton moravicus 82
Lyssacina 50
Lystrosaurus murrayi 106

Machairodus cultridens 238
Mammuthus columbi 276
Mammuthus imperator 278
Mammuthus primigenius 274
Mammuthus primigenius fraasi 272
Mammuthus trogontherii 270
Marrolithus ornatus 58
Mastodon americanus 280
Mastodonsarus giganteus 116
Medusae 52
Megaloceros giganteus 296
Meganeura monyi 74
Merychippus primus 244
Merycoidodon culbertsoni 218
Mesohippus bairdii 212
Mesosaurus tenuidens 96
Metamynodon planifrons 222
Metriorhynchus brachyrhynchus 142
Mixosaurus carnalius 102

Moeritherium lyonsi 232
Monoclonius nasicornus 124
Mosasaurus mosasauroides 144
Mystriosaurus bollensis 140

Nannopterygius entheciodon 156
Neocathartes sp. 180
Nothosaurus procerus 104

Omphyma grandis 60
Orthoceratids 62
Oxyaena lupina 202

Palaeobatrachus grandipes 178
Palaeolodus ambiguus 186
Palaeoloxodon antiquus 266
Palaeoloxodon falconeri 268
Palaeomeryx kaupi 242
Palaeotapirus helveticus 250
Panthera spelaea 292
Paradoxides gracilis 54
Parexus 70
Parvancorina 48
Phenacodus primaevus 208
Phororharcos inflatus 184
Placodermi 68
Placodus gigas 98
Platybelodon grangeri 258
Plesiosaurus sp. 148

310

'Proavis' 166
Protolyella 52
Protospongia 54
Psammolepis paradoxa 66
Pseudocynodictis
    gregarius 206
Pteranodon ingens 164
Pteraspis rostrata 66
Pterichthys 68
Pterodactylus antiquus 162
Ptychoparia striata 56

Rangea 48
Rangifer tarandus 300
Rhamphorhynchus
    gemmingi 160

Saltoposuchus longipes 108
Sauroctonus progressus 94
Scutosaurus karpinskii 92
Scyphocrinites excavatus 64
Seymouria baylorensis 86
Spriggina 48
Stenopterygius
    quadridiscus 154

Tarbosaurus bataar 130
Teleoceras fossiger 252
Tetralophodon
    angustidens 256
Thylacosmilus atrox 236
Trachodon annectens 132

Triadobatrachus
    massinoti 114
Triassochelys dux 110
Tribrachidium 48
Triceratops prorsus 126
Triconodon mordax 174
Tylosaurus dyspelor 146
Tyrannosaurus rex 128

Uintatherium mirabile 226
Ursus spelaeus 294

Varanosaurus acutirostris 90

Xenacanthus decheni 72

Zeuglodon cetoides 234